# DAYS IN THE SUN

# *Days in the Sun*

JEAN HEAD

*and*

LESLIE SCRASE

ILLUSTRATED BY

*David Grice*

LONDON

EPWORTH PRESS

FIRST PUBLISHED IN 1967 BY

EPWORTH PRESS

*Book Steward*
FRANK H. CUMBERS

SET IN MONOTYPE BASKERVILLE AND PRINTED IN GREAT BRITAIN BY THE CAMELOT PRESS LTD LONDON AND SOUTHAMPTON

# *Contents*

## DAYS IN THE AFRICAN SUN

BY JEAN HEAD



## DAYS IN THE INDIAN SUN

BY LESLIE SCRASE

JEAN HEAD

# DAYS IN THE AFRICAN SUN

*Stories of children of Southern Nigeria*

For Mary Sennitt and Dora Skipsey who will recognize themselves in these stories

# *About the People*

Nigeria is a huge country, six and a half times as big as England and Wales. The great River Niger and its tributary the River Benue divide the country into three regions: the North, and to the south, the West and East Regions. People of the Yoruba tribe have their home in the West, those of the Ibo and Efik tribes in the East, whilst the Hausa tribe is found in the vast Northern region. Each tribe has its own distinctive names for its children, and all names are given with thought for their meanings.

The following stories have Yoruba settings with Yoruba names: 'Market Day', 'Sunday', 'Monday', 'Tuesday', 'Thursday', 'Friday', and 'Saturday'. Most Yoruba names are used in an abbreviated form.

Hospitals and schools in the Eastern Region would have patients and children from a mixture of tribes. However, 'Wednesday' is a story containing Ibo names, whilst the stories 'Christmas Day' and 'New Year's Eve' are about Efik people.

Moslems have their own names for their children; for example, those found in the story 'Friday'.

Amongst Christian families names are often given from the Bible, the Old as well as the New Testament. The Christian virtues are also often used as names. The days of the week are also used, particularly Sunday, if a child is born on that day. Examples are found in the stories 'New Year's Eve' and 'Sunday'.

# *How to pronounce the Names*

The names are easy to pronounce as all syllables and letters are sounded and carried smoothly on from one to the next. No one syllable is stressed more than another.

YORUBA NAMES

*New Year's Eve*

| | |
|---|---|
| Bolaji: | Bol (as in *boll*ard) -aj (as in b*adg*e) -i (as in *i*t) |
| Esan: | E (as in p*e*t) -san (as *song*) |

*Market Day*

| | |
|---|---|
| Titilola: | Ti (as in *ti*ll) -ti (as in *ti*ll) -lo (as in *lo*t) -la (as *lu* in *lu*ll) |
| Mr Lebi: | Le (as in *le*t) -bi (as in *bi*t) |
| Shango: | Shang (to rhyme with *hang*) -go (as in *goa*t) |

*Sunday*

| | |
|---|---|
| Simbo: | Sim (to rhyme with *him*) -bo (as in peep-*bo*) |
| Mr Bajulaiye: | Baj (as *badge*) -u (as *oo* in b*oo*t) -laiy (as *lie*) -e (as *i* in *i*t) |
| Moyeni: | Moy (to rhyme with *boy*) -eni (as *any*) |

*Monday*

| | |
|---|---|
| Olufemi: | O (as in b*oa*t) -lu (as in *loo*se) -fe (as in *fe*ll) -mi (as in *mi*ss) |
| Mr Josiah: | Jo (as in *jo*lt) -siah (as *sire*) |
| Agbeke: | Ag (as in b*ag*) -bek (as *beck*) -e (as *i* in *i*t) |
| Dupe: | Du (as *do*) -pe (as in *pe*ck) |

*Tuesday*

| | |
|---|---|
| Dayo: | Day (as *die*) -o (as in p*o*t) |

Mr Adeyemo: A (as *ah*) -de (as *day*) -ye (as in y*e*s) -mo (as in *mo*ss)

Mr Jolaosho: Jol (as in *jol*ly) -a (as *ay*) -osh (as in t*osh*) -o (as in g*o*)

Tokunboh: Tok (as *took*) -un (as in s*un*) -boh (as in peep-*bo*)

*Thursday*

Ireti: I (as in *i*t) -re (as *ray*) -ti (as in *ti*ll)

Ade: A (as *ah*) -de (as *day*)

Atoke: A (as *u* in g*u*n) -tok (as *tock*) -e (as *ay*)

Mr Atilade: At (as in h*at*) -il (as *ill*) -a (as *ah*) -de (as *day*)

Abiodun: A (as in h*a*t) -bi (as in *bi*t) -o (as in r*o*se) -dun (to rhyme with a shortened and rather nasal *sung*)

Olufunmilayo: O (as in r*o*se) -lu (as in *loo*se) -fun (as *dun* above) -mi (as in *mi*ss) -lay (as *lie*) -o (as in p*o*t)

Laide: La (as *lie*) -i (as in *i*t) -de (as *day*)

Remi: Re (as in *re*st) -mi (as in *mi*ss)

*Friday*

Mr Olumide: O (as in r*o*se) -lu (as in *loo*se) -mi (as in *mi*ss) -de (as *day*)

*Saturday*

Lolade: Lol (as *loll*) -a (as *u* in g*u*n) -de (as *day*)

Dapo: Da (as in *da*d) -po (as in *po*t)

Taiwo: Tai (as *tie*) -wo (as in *wo*ke)

Kehinde: Kehin (as *kine*) -de (as *di* in *di*g)

Rev A. Ayorinde: Ay (as *igh* in s*igh*) -or (as in f*or*) -inde (as in *Indie*s)

Mr Idowu: Id (as in h*id*) -o (as in b*oa*t) -wu (as *woo*)

## IBO NAMES

*Wednesday*

Nnenna: Nnenn (to rhyme with *hen*) -a (as *u* in g*u*n)

Alaezi: A (as in c*a*t) -laez (as *laze*) -i (as in *i*t)

Miss Oko: O (as in b*oa*t) -ko (as *coa* in *coa*l)

### EFIK NAMES

*Christmas Day*

| | |
|---|---|
| Effiong: | Eff (as in *eff*ort) -i (as in *i*t) -ong (as in s*ong*) |
| Arit: | A (as in c*a*t) -rit (as in *writt*en) |
| Abia: | A (as in c*a*t) -bi (as in *bi*t) -a (as in c*ar*d) |
| Nkoya: | N (as in *n*et) -koy (as *coi* in *coi*l) -a (as *u* in gun) |
| Asuquo: | A (as *u* in g*u*n) -su (as *sou* in *sou*p) -quo (as in *quo*ta) |
| Bassey: | Bass (as in *bas*ket) -ey (as *y* in ver*y*) |
| Akon: | A (as in c*a*t) -kon (as in *con*ker) |

*New Year's Eve*

| | |
|---|---|
| Mr Ndyio: | N (as in *n*et) -dyi (as *die*) -o (as in p*o*t) |

### MOSLEM NAMES

*Friday*

| | |
|---|---|
| Shifawu: | Shif (as in *shif*t) -aw (as *ow* in c*ow*) -u (as *oo* in l*oo*se) |
| Raheem: | Ra (as in *ra*ther) -heem (to rhyme with *seam*) |
| Mr Lawal: | La (as *lu* in *lu*ck) -wal (to rhyme with *pal*) |
| Ali: | Al (as in p*al*) -i (as in *i*t) |

# *Christmas Day*

'Come on Effiong, this is no time for sleep.' Effiong opened his eyes and smiled. 'I wasn't asleep, just resting and thinking nice things,' he said. 'You nurses woke us so early this morning.'

'Yes, we did—but we wanted to sing carols in each ward before we hurried through all the work that was waiting. Well—is Christmas Day in hospital fun?'

Effiong smiled again. This young nurse, whose name was Arit, belonged to his tribe and she had been especially kind to him since he was admitted to the hospital ten days ago. All the nurses were terribly busy—the hospital was the only one for very many miles and it was always overcrowded—but Nurse Arit had often made time to come and talk to him. She had even popped in to see him during her afternoon off, on the day he realized that he would be spending Christmas away from his own home.

'You'll enjoy it—you see,' she had reassured him, and he had been a little comforted.

Now he was beginning to realize that she was right.

He and the other children in his ward had watched fascinated during the last few days as the nurses had decorated their ward. Coloured papers had been strung across the ceiling, a balloon had been hung over each cot and in the centre of the long wall was a big picture of Jesus as a baby, with His parents and the three Kings giving their gifts. Effiong loved this picture—one of the Kings was an African and he had an African boy with him about his own size.

If only his own parents and his big brother and little sister could be with him, it would be just perfect he thought. But his own village of Okigwe was many miles away and since his father brought him here (and what a bumpy ride in the lorry it had been, and how ill he had felt) none of his family had been able to visit him. He was so very grateful to Nurse Arit for her friendship.

'You're coming outside, Effiong, now,' Arit was saying. 'Look, I'm going to lift little Abia and Nkoya into your cot and the other nurses and I will push you outside. Abia and Nkoya are both of your tribe—you can pretend they are your sisters and look after them.'

Effiong laughed with delight. He held the two little girls' hands as they reached the end of the ward and were pushed through the big doors on to the verandah outside. What a noise! The four wards of the hospital made the sides of a square with a big open space in the centre. All the patients except the very ill were being brought into this open space; some to sit in chairs, some to lie propped up in their cots and beds, so that they could see and hear all that was going on. There were nurses everywhere, all laughing and smiling, and all doing their best to see that the patients were as happy and comfortable as they could be.

Opposite him Effiong could see the mothers who had come to the hospital for the birth of their babies. Usually the babies were left in little canvas cradles, but today they were in their mothers' arms. 'Just like the picture in our ward,' thought Effiong.

Then suddenly everyone was quiet. The Sister of the hospital and a Methodist minister had arrived.

They all loved the Sister. She was a white woman who had come from England very many years ago to be in charge of this hospital. No doctor lived at the hospital and often the Sister had to do things which only a skilful doctor would have done in a bigger hospital. All the children, and many of the grown-ups too, called her 'Ma'—she was like a mother to them all. The minister, the Reverend Asuquo Bassey, looked so happy, and Effiong knew why. He and his wife had come to the hospital some days ago to stay, and both of them had spent a lot of time in the wards talking to the patients. Mrs Bassey had told Effiong and the other children exciting stories and she had taught them new songs to sing too.

Mrs Bassey had come to have her baby whilst under the Sister's care and word had quickly gone round this morning that their baby son had been born during Christmas night. What a happy Christmas for them! Everyone in the hospital shared their joy.

Mr Bassey led a short service and somehow they all found it easier to worship the Baby who was born so long ago in Bethlehem as they looked across at Mrs Bassey nursing her first-born son as she sang.

Then Mr Bassey went over to sit by his wife and the Sister stood up. 'This afternoon', she said, 'we hope as many as possible will have their families to visit them, but now the nurses and I are doing our best to make you happy this Christmas Day. We have a little present for each of you. Come, nurses, with your scissors and help me cut them off the tree.'

There had been so much to hear and see and join in that Effiong had scarcely noticed the big Cassia tree under whose shade the minister had stood for the service. Now he saw that balloons danced from it and that it was covered in little parcels wrapped in blue, pink, white, yellow, and green paper. Someone had been very busy getting everything ready and Effiong wondered how it had been managed with the ordinary work of the hospital as well. No wonder Sister's smiling face sometimes looked very tired, just as he remembered his mother's face looking tired at the end of the day.

The white parcels were coming down. Effiong saw that they were all going to the babies. Mrs Bassey was given one first because her son was the newest baby of all. Then the nurses began to come over to the children. Abia and Nkoya had pretty pink parcels and Effiong was given a blue one. He was so excited he could scarcely undo it, and he had to stop in the middle to help Abia, who couldn't manage to slip the string off hers. His shaking fingers managed it at last, and there it was, a gay red plastic lorry, the first toy he had ever had. He was so happy he could have cried, and he saw Nkoya was crying a little as she and Abia clasped tiny dolls. They had never even seen a doll before they played with the toys in the big box in their ward, and they certainly never dreamed of owning one. Then Effiong saw something sticking out of the wrapping paper and found they had each missed a card tucked in with their presents. He gave the little girls theirs and looked at his own. It was a picture of Jesus as a baby for him to keep and take home.

'Well, Effiong, how are you today?' Sister and Mr Bassey were coming round and talking to each patient.

'Oh, thank you, thank you, Ma,' Effiong said excitedly. 'I shall keep this lorry and this card all my life to remind me of your kindness to us.'

Then the noise and bustle began again as the cots and beds were wheeled back into the wards. The nurses came to each child and tucked them down for a rest. After the morning's excitement they were soon all fast asleep, all clutching their precious gifts from the tree.

Effiong woke gradually and could not think where he was. He was lying in his hospital cot but surely that was his mother's voice—and Akon's, his little sister's chatter? He sat up with a jerk and there they were—his whole family, squatting by his side, waiting quietly for him to wake.

'Mother, Father,' he began; and he was off, telling them all that had happened during Christmas morning and each day since his arrival in the ward.

'It is good here,' said his father, when at last an excited Effiong had finished his story. 'We miss you at home, and we cannot come again to see you till I come to fetch you away, but the nurse says that will not be long now, and she says they are making you quite strong again. It is good here. The Sister is a good mother to you. See, we have brought her a gift of pineapples and eggs. You will give them to her when we have gone. We have a long journey home and we must go now. We know you are in good hands here. Good-bye my son. A happy Christmas.'

'Good-bye father. Good-bye mother.' Effiong's eyes were shining with happiness. 'Good-bye, good-bye. For me it has been a very happy Christmas Day. I am almost glad to be ill so that I have been able to share Christmas at this hospital.'

## *New Year's Eve*

Daniel fingered his trumpet and looked at it lovingly. He wiped away a speck of dust with his khaki shirt. His trumpet? It belonged to the band, but he was going to save as hard as he possibly could to try to buy it for himself. Then when he returned to his home he could take it with him. What a thrill that would be! So as soon as school was over each day he went to the carpenter's shop and stayed there as long as he could. It meant he missed some fun with the other boys, but it would be worth it if only he could have that trumpet for his very own. One of the skilled carpenters in the workshop, a man of his own tribe called Godwin, had noticed Daniel's keenness and was teaching him to make lockers and chairs. There were always some to be mended or new ones to be made for the hospital.

Yes, Daniel lived in a special kind of hospital, where all the hundreds of patients, men and women, boys and girls, were lepers. Only those who were very ill or who had bad ulcers were kept in the actual hospital building. All the others lived in little huts, grouped together into men's and women's towns. They lived a normal life—the children went to school, and the men and women worked in the fields or collected palm-kernels from the oil-palm trees, ready to be crushed in their own factory, to give palm-oil.

But they all stayed together in the big leprosy

settlement so that the doctors could see them frequently and give them treatment, and so that they did not pass the disease on to other people.

Daniel had been living in the settlement for nine months now. He would never forget the beginning of it all. It had been the week after his twelfth birthday. The evening meal was over in his home and his father, the village schoolmaster, had read from the Bible for their evening prayers. Daniel's younger brothers and sisters had gone off to bed, his mother was busy with the cooking-pots and only he and his father and his aged grandmother were left in the room.

Daniel's father called him over. 'Shut your eyes a minute, son,' he said.

Daniel had wondered whatever game this was, but he did as he was told.

In a minute his father said: 'All right; now open them and tell me what happened.'

Daniel looked surprised, and answered: 'Nothing father. I didn't hear or feel anything.'

His father seemed strangely upset and asked him again if he was sure he had felt nothing. Daniel was quite sure.

Quietly his father had begun to speak and Daniel had listened, his eyes getting bigger and bigger and his heart thumping more and more. 'My son, we did well to give you the name Daniel. We have often read the story together and you know how God helped Daniel long ago and saved him from the lions. Now it is your turn to show that you too are brave. For a while now I have seen that little patch of raised skin on your wrist. It is growing bigger and it is scaly. When your eyes were shut I tickled you on that spot with a feather and you say you felt nothing. My son, we must go to a doctor to make sure, but if I am right you have leprosy.'

Daniel's grandmother had been listening quietly, but when she heard the last word—'leprosy'—she let out a terrible shriek and began to rock herself backwards and forwards, wailing as she did so.

'Peace, woman, peace,' said Daniel's father sternly. 'Do you want to frighten the boy? There is no need for your wailing. We know that your brother was a leper and that he died after many years of great pain and that your village turned him out to live as an animal in the bush. But things have changed. God has sent the white man with his medicines. Our own people are being taught how to cure this illness. No longer is it to be feared. Daniel will have to go away from us, but he will be well cared for and it will not be long before he is cured, and we shall pray to the good Lord for him every day till he comes home again.'

That was nine months ago.

The time had gone very quickly and happily, although of course he longed to be home again. His father wrote to him every week with news of the family and the village. Every night at bedtime he pictured them sitting round for evening prayers—father and mother, grandmother, his cousin David, his brothers, Sunday and Isaac, and his sisters, Comfort and Mercy. Then he would say his prayers too, thanking God that he was getting better, thanking Him, before he fell asleep, that the terror had gone from the word 'leper'.

He *was* getting better, there was no doubt about it. When his father had brought him (it was fifty miles from home and they had taken two days to come with Daniel on the crossbar of his father's bicycle) the doctor had received them kindly.

'You have done well,' he said. 'The boy has the disease only very slightly. How wise you were to bring him at once. You need have no fear. We will look after him and as soon as he is well he shall come home to you.'

The doctor was the first white man to whom Daniel had spoken, but he didn't feel nervous with him, his smile and twinkling eyes stopped that.

Every Wednesday afternoon Daniel joined the long queue of boys to see the doctor. When it was his turn the doctor would chat for a few minutes, look at Daniel's skin and give him his tablets for the week. Those who had been there for several years said that the nurses used to give them painful injections, but now all they had to do was to remember to take their precious white tablets.

The doctors took no chances. For some time after the skin had healed they took tests and looked into their microscopes, and even after the cured patients were allowed to go home, they were asked to come back once or twice for the doctor to see them again.

Today was New Year's Eve. It was time to change into his best white shorts and shirt. Daniel was excited. The band had been practising for hours in the past weeks for today. He, Daniel, was going to help in the celebrations, by blowing his trumpet—and how he would blow it. For New Year's Eve was the great day when the names of the patients who were going to be discharged were read out. So many were hoping and praying that they would hear their names.

Daniel knew his name wasn't on the list—the doctor had told him last week, but he had added that if all went well he would hear his name a year from now.

So today Daniel would do his best to make things

happy for those who would be going home cured tomorrow, to start life again. Certainly it would be a happy new year for them.

Daniel gave his trumpet a final polish and went along to the open space where people were beginning to gather. It was four o'clock and the lists would not be read out until five, but the band was going to play whilst people arrived, and besides, Daniel wanted to see all that was going on. Tomorrow he would have to write two long letters describing it all. One would go home and the other to a new friend called Bolaji Esan.

Bolaji had written several times to him and each letter seemed more of a wonderful surprise to Daniel. Daniel was an Efik, and Bola and his friends were Yorubas, members of a big powerful tribe in the west of the country. Daniel was a boy from a tiny village, and although he enjoyed school and did his best he wasn't very near the top in the end of term Standard 5 exams. Yet Bola told him that he and his friends were students at a great University in the city of Ibadan. They were studying hard to become doctors and lawyers and teachers, but they were also Christians, and they were sending money to the doctor in charge of Daniel to pay for his treatment. When Daniel was well, they wrote, they would adopt another boy and support him. Daniel could not get over the wonder of it. Yes, they must be told all about today, and how Daniel hoped he would be on the list next year. Daniel prayed for these new friends of his every night.

No more time to think about them now though, because here was Mr Ndyio the bandmaster. Many boys wanted to join the band but only a few were needed and Daniel knew he must always do his very best or someone else might be given his place. For an hour they played whilst the crowd began to gather. They played hymns and marches and dances; a mixture of Efik and Ibo and English tunes. Daniel enjoyed it all so much, but he was ready to stop and get his breath back when at last the doctors and senior nurses came along the path and sat down behind a little table.

The doctor with the twinkling eyes stood up and began to speak. 'Many years ago,' he said. 'when I first came to this settlement, perhaps I would have ten names to read out on this day, perhaps fifteen. We could do very little to cure you then, we could only dress your sores and make the pain less. Today,' he went on, 'I have nine hundred and eighty names on my list. The little white tablets that we give you each week are one of the greatest gifts to man that scientists have ever discovered. Tonight in our Watchnight service we shall give thanks to God. Tomorrow nine hundred and eighty of you will leave us to live your lives with your families again. Those of you who are left, do not despair: there is hope that all of you will be cured.'

A great shout went up from the crowd. Everyone clapped and cheered, and as Mr Ndyio lifted his hand Daniel and the other trumpeters blew a great note of delight as their way of giving thanks.

# *Market Day*

Titilola enjoyed school, but today it was a relief to hear the bell ringing and to know that it was one o'clock. With the other children in Standard 5 she stood by her desk and then all forty of them marched out of their classroom, placing their Yoruba reading-books in a neat pile on the teacher's desk as they went past. The whole primary school of two hundred and fifty children always came together for a few minutes before they went home. Class by class with their teachers they marched out to the rhythm of the drums of their own school drummers, singing Yoruba songs as they went. As many as could crowded their lines under the shade of the two big breadfruit trees growing side by side at the edge of the compound because the heat was intense at one o'clock. The sandy ground almost burnt their toes it was so hot. Very few of the children wore any shoes.

Their Principal, Mr Lebi, came and stood in front of them and they were suddenly quiet. Sometimes he had notices to give out, or messages for their parents, but today he only said a short prayer and dismissed them. Often he said the prayer in Yoruba, his voice rising and falling with the tones of the words, but today he said it in English, speaking slowly to give the children in Standard 1, who had only just started to learn English, a chance to follow the meaning.

Titilola was glad to get away and she hurried down the path to the main road that ran from Yaba into the heart of the city of Lagos. If she had stayed behind talking to her friends there would have been a great queue of children by the time she got to the bus stop, and she would probably have had to wait a long time. In any case some of the conductors weren't very kind to schoolgirls and sometimes thought it a joke to leave them behind when there was room on the bus.

Today was market day and Titi had to go straight to the big Jankara market where her mother had been selling at their stall all morning. Her mother depended on her to take over for the afternoon whilst she went home to prepare the food and look after the younger children. Until the white man came, bringing with him his seven-day week, the Yoruba people had always had a five-day week, and their markets still opened once every five days instead of on a regular day in each 'Sunday-to-Saturday' week.

Titi didn't mind selling at their stall. In fact it was rather fun and she was happy that her mother thought her responsible enough to leave her in charge. But she did get very tired—especially if Market Day fell on a Thursday or a Friday when she was already tired by a week at school. Today it was Monday so she felt fresher after a weekend at home. Lessons began at school at eight o'clock every morning and to be sure of being there in time she had to leave her home just after seven. Often before that she had swept the house and given her younger brothers and sisters their breakfast whilst her mother looked after the new baby. She had home-work to do every day for school too and there was very little spare time on market days. She did keep her books with her and sometimes managed to read a little when there were not many people about. She would have to watch out, she knew. If she didn't work hard this year she would have no chance of passing the entrance examination to a secondary school and she did so want to go to one of the good ones in Lagos.

She had reached the market now—all the stalls were arranged under a great high black corrugated iron roof and it always seemed a bit dark till your eyes got used to it.

Here was their stall, and her mother was already collecting her things, and making sure the cloth holding her sleeping baby on to her back was secure.

'The market is busy today, Titi,' her mother said when they had greeted each other. 'I hope you will sell a lot, but be careful and watch the money you take. See here is the little bag. When you have changed from your school tunic, remember to hide the money-bag in the folds of the cloth round your waist. I will be back before dark to help you pack up.'

'Not much chance of reading books today,' thought Titi. She would have to stay up late tonight or get up even earlier than usual in the morning. If she did that though, sometimes she fell asleep at her desk in school, and then there was trouble from the teacher. 'Never mind,' she said to herself, 'my family must come first and it is more important that my brothers should get to secondary school than my sister and me.'

How noisy it was today. Her mother was right—there were more people about than usual. She wished someone would come and buy from her. She was hungry and her mother always let her spend a few pennies from her first sale on something to eat. She had had nothing since her breakfast before seven o'clock this morning and she would not have a proper

meal until after dark, at about seven o'clock tonight. Her mother would prepare a big meal for them all then—and after it she would be more ready for sleep than home-work.

Her mother had a very mixed stall. Some things for sale came from Nigeria, some were brought from up-country by travelling traders, others were made in Lagos. There were beads of many different colours and sizes: polished red stones, strung together in the North; shiny wooden ones from the villages a few miles away, each bead beautifully carved. There were little lumps of shiny black ore called 'tiro', which the Yoruba women crushed to powder to make attractive black marks round their eyes. From the Hausa people of the North came pretty little red leather pouches full of the crushed tiro and there were little painted pieces of bone to apply the powder. Her father carved these in the long evenings at home—he used a sharp pen-knife and if he had plenty of time he made a different pattern on each tiny handle. He made bone crochet-hooks too for them to sell, and each of these had an intricate pattern on its handle. Her brother enjoyed painting the large wooden hair-combs which father made, and inventing his own bright patterns for them.

When Titi was a little girl and could first remember coming to the market they only sold things which they had made themselves, or which had been found or made in other parts of Nigeria. But now they sold more and more things from other parts of the world. Plastic bags and belts came from Japan; bright metal brooches and little china animals from England; straw hats, sandals and bags from the Canary Islands.

They looked gay and inviting, Titi thought, and she hoped her customers would think so too; but they didn't last like the things they made at home and they soon lost their brightness.

At last a woman came over to her stall, and it was a big plastic shopping-bag that caught her eye.

'I'll have a red one,' she said—and Titi clutched the precious shilling. Now she could eat! She called to two little boys standing near. They too had finished school for the day and had been sent to sell in the market for the afternoon. They each had a large basket on their heads and they lowered them for Titi to look inside. With one penny Titi bought three bananas; with another she bought two oranges, half peeled and with a slice cut off the top, so that she could suck the juice. She hadn't realized how thirsty she was till she saw and smelt the oranges. Another penny bought a big cob of maize which the boys' mother had roasted at home and it was still warm. Titi thought she might spend one more penny and chose three flat fried fufu cakes. The tomatoes and green ochra looked nice, but the fufu would be more filling.

The little boys went off happily. It was their first sale, and they dare not go home till their baskets were empty. Titi put the change carefully in her little bag and tucked it out of sight and settled down to enjoy herself. She felt better when she had eaten and though she was still a little hungry she decided to keep an orange and the last banana for later on. Her mother would not expect her to spend any more money—and she would know exactly what had been sold from the stall and how much money Titi should have. Her mother had never been to school and could not read or write, but she could do amazing sums with money in her head and she had a wonderful memory for the exact amount of her stock and its prices.

After the first little while Titi didn't usually notice the noise but today there seemed more than usual. She looked round and thought she saw a lot of movement in a crowded corner of the market. The crowd was coming her way and the leaders were drumming. Then she realized what was happening and leant forward to watch. In the centre of the group was a tall woman dressed in a leather jerkin with many cowrie shells sewn on in a pattern. She was dancing slowly, holding an earthenware pot in her raised left hand. There was a small fire in the pot and Titi knew she was a priestess of the god Shango, the fire god. Her attendants were going from stall to stall with little bowls collecting money from other Shango worshippers. Titi shook her head when they came to her. She and her family were Christians and she went to a Christian school, but all the same she was quite relieved when the priestess and her followers had gone on and left her in peace. One never quite knew what might happen with such folk about.

The extra people certainly helped trade and Titi was busy selling for the next hour or so. Her mother would be pleased and Titi wondered whether there would be enough money to spare this week to buy her a khaki tunic for school. Hers was so short and had been mended and mended. Her school friend's mother had a sewing-machine and said she would make it for her if she could buy the cloth and the red buttons to go on the shoulders.

It was beginning to get dark and Titi ate the rest of the fruit. Her mother would be here soon and in half an hour the whole busy market would be quiet and empty—until another five days brought Market Day again.

# *Sunday*

'Come along, it's nearly time for morning service.' Simbo began to bang a long iron bar hanging from the branch of a tree outside the church in the little village of Igbogbo. It made a good noise and the hens and two little brown dogs which had been scratching around in the dusty earth near the church door scuttled off behind the nearest hut. Seeing the hens reminded Simbo of her own hen shut up in a box at home. She had just hatched six eggs and tomorrow when there was more time Simbo knew she must get some pink dye and colour the little fluffy chicks before letting the family loose. That would protect them, she hoped, from the quick eyes of the hawk which often soared over their village.

She went on clanging now, and first the children and then the men and women began to arrive. No one hurried, it was too hot, even at ten o'clock in the morning, but soon the church was nearly full. The children sat at the front, the men on the left side and the women on the right. The men had backs to their forms but the women sat on backless benches, otherwise the babies comfortably tied on their mothers' backs would have had their faces squashed.

Perhaps a few more of the villagers than usual came to church today because the village had visitors for the weekend. Ten young men from the Teacher Training College eight miles away were camping in the nearby primary school. Simbo's father, Mr Bajulaiye, was one of the class leaders of the Church so he had helped to arrange the visit and Simbo knew that the young men were members of the Student Christian Movement at their college. Simbo and her friends had hung around the school doorway watching curiously all that had gone on last evening. They had helped by making several journeys to the stream to fetch buckets of water for them, and they had collected wood for their fire. They had been surprised and had whispered amongst themselves as they watched the students kindle a fire and roast themselves some cobs of maize for their supper. The children had come to peep in again earlier this morning and had seen the students roll up their bedding, sweep the floor and tidy up after their breakfast.

'Fancy men doing such things,' Moyeni had said to Simbo. 'My big brothers and my father would have sat and watched whilst I helped mother do that kind of work. Our men clean the bush for the farm and harvest the crops, but we girls and women have to look after the home and cook and weed and hoe the farm as well. Sometimes I wish I was a boy so I didn't have to do so much, but these young men don't seem to mind what they do.'

The students were friendly and their leader, Solomon, had come over to talk to Simbo. He had asked her about school and her brothers at home. He asked her which hymns she liked to sing and had shown her his Yoruba hymn-book. Simbo had never held one before. She knew many hymns off by heart and when they had one in a service which was not well known the catechist called out the words of the verses line by line and they all sang it after him. Nobody else in church had a book—they were too expensive to buy and many of the adults had never been to school and could not read. Solomon had promised to have one of Simbo's favourite hymns in this morning's service and Simbo wondered now as she saw the students arrive whether he had remembered. She had no chance to go and ask him as her father came over and told her she had banged long enough and she was to go and sit with the other children in church.

The chief of the village had recently become a Christian and now everyone waited quietly whilst Mr Bajulaiye and Solomon went to tell him that the service was going to start. The chief's compound was near the church and school in the centre of the village so it was not long before he arrived, followed by several of the village headmen. They sat in special seats at the front of the church and a little boy stood by the chief's chair all through the service waving a big fly whisk to keep the air fresh and cool near the chief's head.

The service went on a long time and it was very hot. Some of the younger children got down off the form and curled up on the grass mats on the floor and went to sleep when Vincent began to preach the sermon. Simbo managed to sit still and listen but she was glad when it was over. She enjoyed the collection time best! Because it was a special occasion, her elder brother, Amos, and three of his friends went forward with drums and a shekere to beat out a rhythm. Everyone began to sway in their seats and clap their hands in time. First the children, then the women and even some of the men got up and began to dance to the front of the church with their gifts. Only a very few brought money, and a big heap of oranges, bananas, pawpaw, pineapple, yams, cassava, peppers, grew below the pulpit and then one of the students went over to the chief for his present of a live hen with its feet bound. The students would enjoy that for their supper tonight! It was making so much noise with its clucking that it was a good thing there was only one more hymn before the service ended!

Afterwards Solomon and Vincent went to the chief's compound for their meal and a rather shy student called Philip came to Simbo's home. He had his meal with Mr Bajulaiye and Amos. Simbo would have loved to listen to their talk but it was her job to help her mother serve the food and look after her baby brother. Even when there were no visitors she did not eat with her father. The men always had the choicest part of the stew first, and the women and girls and small children ate up what was left afterwards.

When Philip had gone back to the school her mother said: 'You have helped me well, daughter, now you can go with your friends.'

Simbo ran to call for Moyeni and they were just in time to join the end of the procession headed by the students and Church leaders as it started off round the village. More and more people came out of their homes and they all sang songs and danced as they went, the drums keeping everyone together. The procession stopped in the open space between the school and the church. The sun was high in the sky and those who could, stood under the big mango tree at one end to be in the shade. They went on singing until the students came out of the school again. They were not in their smart white shirts and shorts but were dressed up ready to act some plays.

First they acted the Prodigal Son and everyone laughed when Vincent pulled two of the half-wild pigs which roamed the village into a corner and pretended to be looking after them and sharing their food. It took Simbo longer to guess the next story—what was a finely-dressed student doing with her baby brother? He did not look used to babies, no wonder the baby was crying! Then she realized that it was King Solomon deciding in his wisdom what to do when two mothers claimed the same baby. They ended with The Good Samaritan and then everyone sang some more songs.

Dressed as a student again, Solomon came forward and held up his hand.

'I am not wise like King Solomon,' he said, 'but my friends and I are fortunate to be training as teachers, and because we are Christians we would like to share our good fortune with you. We shall come again often on Sundays and we shall start a Sunday-school for your children.'

He looked over to Simbo and smiled at her and she gave a jump for joy.

'But we want to do more than that,' Solomon went on. 'I have talked to your chief and he says that on Saturday evenings, when we are here, we may help all you mothers and fathers who would like to learn to read. We will be here next Saturday to begin. Children, you must tell your parents that reading is fun and not too hard so that they will want to come and learn. Good-bye, all of you, and thank you for your welcome.'

Everyone began to move away talking excitedly of Solomon's words. Simbo went home and helped her mother grind the peppers for the evening meal. She did not mind the hard work, she had plenty to think about. Then she heard her father calling.

'Simbo,' he said, 'help your mother and then you and Amos can come with me to say good-bye to our guests.

They will go in the morning as soon as it is light to be back at college in time for their studies. It is good that they will come again. They are good friends to our village.'

'I have just finished, father,' answered Simbo. 'It has been the best Sunday I can remember, and soon, I shall go to Sunday-school, and Mother will be able to read like you and Amos and me.'

# *Monday*

Femi reached the village of Coker's Market at nine o'clock on a hot Monday morning. He had already walked five miles from his own village of Ogbe and it was another seven before he reached Ifo, their nearest point on the main tarred road. There he would be able to catch a lorry to take him the fifty miles to Lagos.

How he had longed in recent days for the Monday that meant the return to school for the beginning of a new term. This was the first time he had ever been glad to leave his home at the end of the holidays.

Coker's Market seemed busier than usual and Femi soon saw the reason. A big lorry was standing by the houses and the driver was talking to the village women. Presently they moved away and started carrying baskets of oranges to the lorry. The day before, the women had been out on the farms picking the oranges and now here was the lorry to take them to a big, new factory. Femi had heard about it at school— it was just outside Ibadan and the juice of oranges was tinned and bottled there.

With their bitter, green skins, oranges were familiar enough to Femi and he couldn't understand anyone bothering much with them. But he began to wonder if he could get a lift on the lorry to the main road— it would save him a long hot walk and he'd get there sooner even if he did have to wait a bit till the lorry was full and ready to go.

The driver looked friendly and Femi moved over to where he was standing and greeted him. It was obvious Femi was travelling as he had his few possessions tied up in a cloth and perched on his head. After a bit the driver said that if he could keep his balance on top of a full load of oranges he could go as far as the main road with them. It would be about half an hour before they were ready to go.

Femi was glad of a rest and he moved off a little way to sit in the shade of a tree. He was near enough to keep his eye on the lorry but too far off to have to talk to anyone. He wanted to be alone. He was soon deep in thought.

He had been making this journey back to school three times a year for five years now, ever since he was nine. Femi always enjoyed going back to school, but until this time it had been a wrench to leave home. Things were different now.

Could it only be three months ago that the messenger had come to him at school? He could remember now the dreadful shock it had been, turning him from a boy into a man. His father—dead. Although Femi was only fourteen he was the eldest son, and so he became the head of the family. He had been allowed to go home at once when the news came and he had had to make all the decisions for the family. His father and mother were Christians. He and his brothers and sisters had heard stories about Jesus for as long as they could remember and their parents had helped them to love Him and to follow Him. There weren't many Christians in Ogbe and his uncles were not Christians. They believed that there were spirits all around them waiting to do them harm if they did not keep on the right side of them by frequent gifts.

His father's funeral service had been in the Christian church and the pastor had been a real friend to Femi and his mother. But when the pastor had gone home his senior uncle had come into the house and said:

'Now we will have the ceremony of Second Burial.'

Femi had been horrified and had refused to allow it. It hadn't been easy to say 'No' because he had always been brought up to respect and obey those who were older than he was. But he knew he was right and that his father was safe with God and needed nothing that they could provide to help him on his long journey.

Then he had gone back to school and with his own sadness and the busy life of books and games he hadn't thought much more about his uncles and their pagan customs until he had returned home for this last holiday.

What a difficult and unhappy holiday it had been. Had he been right in the things he had tried to do? No one understood him as his father had done and he had had no one to turn to for advice. What a relief to be going back to school again. He had found himself again and again longing for this Monday. As soon as the first rush of the beginning of term was over he would seek out Mr Josiah and tell him his troubles. He would know how to help.

As soon as he had seen his mother when he had returned home for the holidays he had known something was wrong. She looked so tired and worried and so very different from her usual happy self. That evening after the younger children were asleep she had told him all her troubles. After the funeral when Femi had gone back to school again her relatives and friends in the village had given her no peace.

'It has disgraced the family', they had told her many times, 'not to have had all the ceremonial of the ancestors at the funeral. Look out,' they said, 'the spirits will be angry. They will punish you. If they punish us we will blame you.'

Then things did begin to go wrong. First little Agbeke who was just beginning to walk fell into the fire and her arm had been terribly burnt. Femi's mother had walked ten miles to the nearest clinic to have it dressed and had gone back there with her once a week five times until it had healed. They had been terrible journeys. Dupe, who was twelve, and the eldest girl had had to stay at home from the village school to look after the other children. None of the neighbours would help because they said the spirits were angry. Agbeke was too weak to walk and extremely heavy to carry along the long hot dusty road. The clinic was an outpost of a Christian hospital and the nurses had been very kind. Whilst they were waiting, Femi's mother had heard Christian hymns being sung and it had almost been worth the long journey just for that. It helped her to know that she was right and that Agbeke's burn had been an accident and nothing to do with evil spirits.

The crops on the farm hadn't done too well either. Femi's mother knew it was because they had become choked with weeds. With no husband to do anything and with Agbeke needing nursing she just hadn't had enough time to spend on the farm. The villagers said it was the spirits again.

Femi's mother was so glad to have her big son at home. Together they had prayed to God every evening. They talked about the meaning of his name, Olufemi, though people rarely used the first part. It

DG

meant 'The Lord loves me', and they knew it was true even though things were so difficult at present.

Femi had asked his mother if she wanted him to give up school and to stay at home and help her with the other children and the farm. But his mother said that he must go back and she would manage. He could be more use to them all when he had finished his training and they knew his father would have wanted him to stay at school.

He hadn't been really convinced and he had kept turning the problem over in his mind. He felt so responsible for them all. The villagers hadn't spared him either. They, and his relatives, kept telling him it was all his fault. They said worse things would happen.

Five nights ago something far worse had happened. Yinka, his six-year-old brother, hadn't been well all day. He had been very sick and they had wondered if he had been eating poisonous berries in the bush. Until he slept, Femi was nursing him. After a while he thought he was asleep. He had moved from his cramped position and Yinka hadn't stirred. The terrible truth had dawned on Femi. His little brother had died in his arms.

It was no good. His mind told him that Yinka had eaten poisonous berries. His mother believed that and she had stayed so calm in her sadness, saying that Yinka was safe with Jesus. But another voice would not keep silence in Femi's head. Were his uncles right after all? Were the spirits angry? Was it all his fault because he had insisted on a Christian burial for his father? He was beginning to wonder.

It was easy enough to be a Christian at school where they had prayers every day and discussions in scripture lessons, and the masters were always ready to help. It had been easy at home in Ogbe when his father had been alive. Family prayers had been so real. How he had missed his father reading a psalm to him before he had come away this morning. It had always seemed the perfect end to happy holidays. He had never imagined it could be so difficult to go on being a Christian as it had been during these last four weeks. Could he go on? How glad he would be to see Mr Josiah and his school friends.

The noise of an engine startled him. He jumped up and ran with his bundle to the lorry.

'Thought you'd gone to sleep and decided not to come,' said the driver. 'Climb up on top quickly.'

The lorry started and it was all Femi could do to keep his balance by clinging on to the roof of the cab as the oranges rolled about and the lorry bumped its way over the rough surface. He had no more time for thinking now, but his face was happier. He was on his way back to the school he loved to find the help he so sorely needed.

# *Tuesday*

'Wake up Dayo, you've slept long enough.'

Dayo opened his eyes and stretched. That was surely his father's voice, but where on earth was he? To begin with he was lying on a bed and he had never known such comfort. At home he slept on a mat on the floor and pulled a cloth up over him. Then he remembered coming to this house last night and he reached for his clothes. He must not waste a minute.

His father was a dispenser, in charge of a small clinic in their village, where he was allowed to give simple medicines and first-aid. Each week a doctor and a nurse came for the day from the big Ilesha hospital, thirty miles away from their village, to treat those who were seriously ill. This doctor had come to Lagos for a week's conference and had brought Dayo's father, Mr Adeyemo, with him, to learn some more and to meet other dispensers. His father's cousin, Mr Jolaosho, lived in Lagos, where he was a chemist, and Dayo had been told he could come for the week too.

They had travelled a hundred and eighty miles yesterday in the back of the doctor's estate car and it had been dark for the last part of the journey. Dayo had been fascinated by the flickering lights of the little oil lamps, often made from empty milk tins, as they passed each tiny village-market at the side of the road they travelled. He had seen a hunter slip into the bush, a lighted candle strapped to his forehead to attract the animals. But he had finally fallen asleep with the motion of the car. He had half woken to strange noises and bright lights, but he was too dazed to do anything except fall asleep again as his father lifted him into the bed at his uncle's home.

Now he went out from the bedroom and greeted his uncle and aunt before standing by his father.

'I have to go now,' said his father. 'I shall see you tonight.'

Dayo's aunt smiled at him.

'I remember how confused I was when my father first brought me to Lagos from a tiny village,' she said. 'Come here and eat and then Tokunboh will take you to see our great city. She is ten, like you, and is on holiday from school till next week when you return to your home.'

Dayo took the big piece of white bread his aunt gave him and drank the cold tea. He could scarcely wait to go and see all that there was outside the house.

Tokunboh laughed at his impatience. 'Don't hurry,' she said. 'You have a week with us—it's not all that exciting anyway. We will go on the bus to Tinubu Square and then I can show you the General Hospital where your father is this morning, and we can go to the Marina.'

Dayo looked even more impatient and surprised. 'A bus? Why can we not walk?' He could not imagine how the city could be so big that his sturdy legs could not take him everywhere in a very short time.

'You'll see,' his cousin answered. 'My father gave me some pennies and told me where to take you.'

When the bus came it looked quite full and the conductor was hanging half outside on the step, but he let

Dayo and Tokunboh squeeze in. The bus jolted off again and Dayo couldn't see anything of where he was going, he was so squashed. It was very hot and noisy too, everyone seemed to be shouting and arguing at the top of their voices. He was very pleased when Tokunboh pulled his hand and they got off with a whole crowd of other people.

'Mind where you go,' said Tokunboh, only just in time. Dayo stepped back and saw that he had nearly fallen into the big open drain that ran alongside the road. His mother had bought him a new pair of shorts and a shirt for this week and he would have ruined them if he had fallen into that black smelly slime at the bottom.

'We'll go and see the big shops first,' said Tokunboh as they walked along. Cars seemed to be dashing every way at once, hooting as they went, and Dayo thought he would never get used to all the noise and bustle. At home the only background sounds they heard were the croaking of frogs and the chirping of crickets. As they turned the corner he stopped and stared. In his village Syrian traders had recently built two new two-storey houses, with an upstairs and a downstairs, and he and his friends had marvelled at them—but these; his head felt it would fall off as he leant back and looked up and up and up. All dazzling white in the sun, with big windows full of glass. What a city! He looked in the shop windows and had to keep asking his cousin what the things were for. His friends at home would find it difficult to believe him when he told them about all these different foods in tins, the brightly coloured clothes, plates and cups, cameras, wirelesses, gramophones, rows and rows of different books, and a whole windowful of exciting-looking children's toys. He had never seen such things.

'Come on,' laughed Tokunboh, 'we have no money and everything here costs a good deal. I want to show you much more yet.'

So Dayo let himself be led away down the hot dusty street, looking all ways as he went.

'Oh, the poor things, Tokunboh,' he cried. 'Look at those blind men!'

Three men, wearing the white long robes and white caps of the Hausa people from Northern Nigeria were going slowly along the pavement. They walked one behind the other, the first holding the hand of a little boy who could see and who was their guide, the other two each with their hand resting on the shoulder of the man in front. The other man, whom Tokunboh had noticed first, was a cripple, crawling along like an animal, with twisted legs and with flat pieces of wood buckled to his knees to protect them as he moved.

'Yes,' said Tokunboh, 'there are many beggars in Lagos. They come down here to beg from the rich people who are going into the big shops. There are still too many parts of our country without clinics and hospitals to help such people when they are young and could be made better.'

'But look—there is the General Hospital where your father's Conference is this week. All those people in the long line are waiting their turn for treatment in the Outpatients' Department.'

Dayo looked in amazement. He had once been with his father to see the new Methodist Hospital at Ilesha and he had thought that was big and wonderful, but this was five times as large. There must be a great many patients needing treatment if they still had to wait in a place as big as this. Tokunboh said that on a busy day you sometimes had to wait for many hours.

There were good doctors inside, but not enough for all the work there was to do.

Tokunboh was talking again and pointing across the road.

'That is the new Government Maternity Hospital,' she said.

Dayo gazed at the great tall building going high into the sky and thought there must be a lot of lucky babies in Lagos.

'Before that was built,' Tokunboh went on, 'mothers with their new babies sometimes had to lie two or three in a bed, the old hospital was so crowded!'

Dayo could have stayed for a long time taking it all in but his cousin wanted to hurry on.

'It's nearly time,' she said.

'Time for what?'

'You come and see.' Off they went again, across the road and on to the Marina. Beautiful houses and gardens, the cathedral, and a big school lined one side of the road, and on the other was the great lagoon. At the edge of the quiet water were canoes, and fishing-nets like sails were hung up on poles to dry. Dayo felt at last he recognized something. But not for long.

'Look,' said Tokunboh excitedly, and as Dayo lifted his eyes he saw an enormous boat, getting larger and larger as it moved quickly towards them. He could see people on the decks waving, looking tiny against the great funnel. He saw the name painted on the side of the boat—*Apapa*.

'That's the name of the wharf over on the other side of the lagoon where the docks are,' Tokunboh explained. 'The mail-boat always sails on a Tuesday, taking people to England. I come as often as I can to see her. Isn't she beautiful?'

They watched till the mail-boat was a tiny shape, crossing the bar of the lagoon and reaching the open sea.

'We must go home now,' said Tokunboh. 'This afternoon you must rest, and tomorrow I shall take you to the big market at Oyingbo. It must be nearly as big as your whole village,' she teased.

On the way home, Tokunboh told Dayo that one day she was going to the United Kingdom on the mail-boat to learn to be a nurse in an English hospital.

'But you mustn't tell my parents,' she ended, 'that's our secret. My father tells me stories about the United Kingdom. He was a pharmacy student in a college there. I was born the year after he returned—that is why I am called Tokunboh.'

'I don't know about mail-boats and England,' said Dayo, 'but I do know that I'm going to work and work when I get back to school so that I can come to this great city to be a student and learn how to help people like those poor beggars we saw. But let's go home now Tokunboh, I've seen and heard so much, and I'm very tired.'

# *Wednesday*

It all began one Wednesday morning in October just after eight o'clock. As soon as morning prayers were over in the school chapel the girls picked up their matchets, collected a few large spades, and went down to the sports field. At least it should have been the sports field, and their job was to begin to make it again. At present all they could see was elephant-grass, waving its feathered plumes five or six feet in the air, and an occasional patch of bracken, a different green but nearly as tall, and with just as firm a hold in the sandy soil.

This was one of the few secondary schools for girls in the area. There were a hundred and fifty girls and nine staff—four African and five European. At least one of the Europeans always seemed to be on leave, so there were never nine staff there at the same time. If only they could have found more teachers, it could have been a bigger school. Each year thirty new girls came into Class I, but nearly a thousand hopefully took the entrance examination for these few places. The school was built near the tiny village of Ikot Inyang, a long way from any town. The dormitories, classrooms and other buildings were scattered over a big compound along the side of a hill. The sports field was the only large flat piece of ground. The whole compound was worked out farmland, so the soil was very poor. But the elephant-grass and the bracken seemed to thrive on it!

The school had not been there very long and in a few more years, the teachers said, they would be able to keep the sports field clear permanently. At present, from November till about May, when the days were hot and dry they could practise running and jumping, play rounders and netball, and all was well. In May and June the rains started, and it rained and rained, often for days on end, till September or October. During this time the plants grew and grew, and the elephant-grass seemed to grow more than anything else!

The whole school did an hour's work somewhere in the compound every Wednesday morning. It was a tiring, dirty start to the day, even though they did have a break afterwards to wash and change from their old clothes into school uniform, and perhaps eat a banana if they were quick, before going to the classrooms for the rest of the morning. The girls didn't mind really—it was good to be able to take a pride in a tidy school compound, and they had some fun. The teachers came with them—indeed the European Principal seemed to work harder than anyone else! The girls all admired her for that.

Nnenna thought back to last January as she walked down the narrow path with the others to where the elephant-grass waved and rustled in the slight breeze. She had been a new girl in Class I then. She had come from a tiny village and had never seen so many girls all at once before. Her brothers had taught her how to run and jump and to her surprise she was better at sports than any other of the new girls. The sports mistress soon noticed her and gave her special coaching.

Although the school sports had been held only six weeks after Nnenna had arrived at the school, she gained many points for her house and she had won the junior high jump, long jump, and 100-yards flat race.

'Well, Nnenna, are you going to practise hard for the sports next term?' Miss Oko was near Nnenna now as they began to pull up the tough green leaves. You had to be careful or the sharp stems cut your fingers, and it was no use leaving the root in the ground—that was asking the grass to shoot up again.

Nnenna decided there was some point in working hard to clear the ground if it meant she could have extra time to get into training. She knew that last March some of the girls from school had travelled nearly two hundred miles to Enugu to take part in inter-school sports and she wanted so much to be one of the party next year.

It took several Wednesdays to get the field clear but at last all the elephant-grass and bracken was piled up ready to be burnt. The girls were promised that the school gardeners would keep an eye on things now and pull up any new stray shoots that still insisted on growing.

Two of the teachers went down after school when the day was getting a little cooler to mark out the ground. Nnenna and one or two of the other keen athletes went to help put in posts and hold the measuring tape. What a time it took! They chose the flattest piece of ground of all for the 100-yards stretch. The 440-yards track went right round the field—there was just room to get it in! Then there was a pit to dig for the long jump landing and sand to bring for it and for the high jump.

By the end of November it was all ready and in the

few weeks before the end of term Miss Oko promised to coach anyone who was interested for an hour before evening prayers, so that they would know how to practise during the holidays. Nnenna was there every single day. It meant she had to work very hard at her lessons too as most of her friends used that time to finish their home-work.

Back home for the holidays, Nnenna discovered that her mother's friends did not think it right for a girl who went to secondary school to spend her time running and jumping. So Nnenna used to slip away with her brother, John, to a clearing in the bush some way from their village, and there they practised together as Miss Oko had taught Nnenna. Several times Nnenna managed a longer jump than John, and he wasn't at all sure he liked being beaten by a girl even if she was his clever sister!

When Nnenna returned to school in January it was the beginning of the new school year and she moved up into Class II. She was careful not to neglect her lessons but every day she managed some time to practise on the sports field. There wasn't a sign of elephant-grass this term. It was hot, even at half-past five when the sun would soon be setting, and the short grass was beginning to look brown and dry. There had been no rain for months. But it was quite pleasant to the toes. Nnenna never wore shoes on the field.

At last it was the day of the school sports. Nnenna was entered again for the 100-yards flat, the high jump and the long jump. It was still four months to her thirteenth birthday so she was able to go in the junior classes. It would have been fun to have entered for some of the other races, to have run with a bottle full of water balanced on her head, or to have joined with Alaezi in the three-legged race. However, it was better to watch these and keep all her energy for the serious events. Nnenna need not have worried. She won the 100-yards easily and not only did she win the junior high jump and long jump, but her long jump of 15 feet 2 inches was a better jump than Caroline's senior winning jump.

Nnenna's ambition was achieved when Miss Oko called her and said she wanted her to be one of the six girls from the school going to Enugu the next week to compete with girls from all the other secondary schools of the region. At Enugu Nnenna managed to add half an inch to her long jump and 15 feet 2½ inches was an official new junior record. Because of this she was chosen to go from the Eastern Region to compete again at Lagos, the capital city, in the All-Nigeria Women's Athletics.

'I'm so glad I did my share of pulling up the elephant-grass on Wednesday mornings,' thought Nnenna, as she went to sleep after the exciting events of the day in Enugu, with more excitement still to come.

# *Thursday*

Ireti hurried along the little path. To one side were the huts of the village of Itohun and she could hear the regular thud as the women pounded the cassava for the day's food. A few yards away on the other side was the lagoon, its still water stretching away across a great expanse, reflecting the great white clouds which today broke the blueness of the sky. Farther along she could see her brother Ade and soon she was near enough to talk to him.

'Have they caught much?' she asked.

Ade was kneeling at the water's edge, a basket of woven grasses by his side. He was stretching into the fish traps made of fine twigs which his father had set below the bank the day before. He turned when he recognized Ireti's voice.

'Yes, we are lucky today,' he said. 'Four big ones, enough for all the visitors. I shall take them home for Atoke to prepare and cook. Are you going for the goat from Mr Atilade?'

'Yes, I'll be back soon,' Ireti answered, and went on along the path towards a house right at the end of the village.

Ade was two years her junior and she knew that her parents had a special love for him because he was their only boy. Ireti was the eldest and she had four sisters. It was because of the youngest, just eight days old today, that the rest of them were so busy. It was her naming ceremony that afternoon and she was to be called Abiodun Olufunmilayo. Afterwards the names would be shortened to Biodun and Funlayo. Ireti was seventeen and she could not remember a time without Ade. He had been born when she was two and she had always helped look after him. She thought back to the birth of all her sisters: Atoke, Laide, Remi, and now the baby. There would have been two more in their family but a second boy and another girl had died when they were only a few months old. Fevers came so suddenly and there was no doctor for many miles, though a nurse did visit the next village once a week now. Ireti thought Biodun was the finest baby they had had. Perhaps it was because her mother had visited this nurse several times in the past months and she had been given good medicines to make the baby healthy. In quiet moments in the past week Ireti had loved to nurse the baby and look at her little pink feet and hands which would soon turn as brown as the rest of her shiny skin.

Thinking of the family she reached Mr Atilade's home and found him sitting outside his doorway. Ireti knelt in greeting and then paused to admire the embroidery he was doing on a new velvet fila, or cap.

'I think that is the best you have ever done,' she exclaimed.

Mr Atilade smiled. 'Yes, it is good, and it is nearly finished. I hope to wear it for your baby this afternoon. If your new sister is as good a girl as you have been she will do well. See, there is your goat. Tell your father he does not have to pay me, it is a present for his sixth child.'

Ireti was so surprised at the praise and the gift that she stood speechless.

'Adupe, adupe pupo,' she managed to say—'Thank you, thank you very much'.

Mr Atilade smiled again.

'Run along then, you will be busy at your house today. What a good thing you are on holiday from school.'

Ireti thanked him once more and untied the rope made from twisted creepers which tethered the goat to a post. She began to lead it back along the path. The goat bleated but followed fairly quietly and Ireti hoped he was not going to be awkward.

She too was glad the new baby had waited for her holidays—or almost—before being born. She and Atoke were at a Methodist boarding school in Ilesha and they had come home last Thursday evening, just a week ago. They had had a long tiring journey of over a hundred miles in bumpy crowded lorries and they still had two miles to walk home from the main road where the second lorry dropped them. Ade was waiting for them when the lorry put them down and they were so glad to see him and to have his help to carry their bundles. He had burst out with the news straight away.

'We have a new sister. She was born this morning. Mother is well. The young girls try to help but we need you and Atoke to look after us.'

It had been a busy week with all the work at home and special services at their church because it was Easter.

Eight days after the birth came the naming ceremony, and here was Thursday again. The baby was to be called Abiodun because she was 'born at a festival', the festival of Easter. Olufunmilayo meant 'the Lord gives me joy'. Certainly the baby had brought joy to them all, and what could be better than the happiness of new life at Easter-time.

As Ireti went on home with the goat she thought about her own name. It meant 'hope' and she was glad there had been so much hope in her life. Eleven years ago a school had been built in her village for the first time and a young teacher had come to live with them. Forty-eight children had started school the first term, but all except four had been boys. Most of the fathers did not think girls were worth sending to school, and they were too useful to their mothers at home. But her father had talked to their minister and then had allowed his first-born daughter to be one of the first pupils.

Ireti had worked hard and had gone on to the secondary school in Ilesha. This was her last year. She took school certificate in November and she did hope she would do well so that she could go to college and train to be a teacher. Ade, Atoke, Laide and Remi had gone in their turn to the village school and the two youngest were still there. Ade was now away in term time at a secondary school in Shagamu, and Atoke, who was eleven, had just finished her first term at Ilesha with Ireti.

She could see her mother now standing at the door of their house, watching for her return. She waved in greeting. It was no use getting fond of this white goat, pretty as he was, because a goat was the proper food to offer to visitors after the naming ceremony. She knew her father would come and kill it for her and get it ready and then she must cook the stew and make sure the feet were specially prepared to present to the guests of honour.

An hour later Ireti stood back from the smoke of the fire. She was tired and hot but everything was ready now and the stew would be tender at the right time for the feast. Ade's fish were fine ones and would give added flavour.

She called to her little sisters who were playing near.

'Run to the lagoon and wash and then come and get ready.'

She wished they had water in pipes with a tap and washrooms as they had at school, but at least the lagoon was near and they didn't have to carry water a long way from the stream.

Soon the whole family was ready, everybody wearing new clothes in honour of their baby. Ireti and Atoke had bought a six-yard piece of printed cotton material each for theirs in the market at Ilesha and had chosen bright colours. They had bought a lovely piece of white embroidered cloth for the baby too. The others were wearing cloths which had been woven in the village, patterned in different shades of blue. The dye came from the indigo plant gathered in the nearby bush. The baby was asleep and they all set off to the village church where the minister was coming to baptize and name the baby. Their friends joined them as they went, and everyone was happy and laughing and talking.

What a wonderful Thursday, thought Ireti, and her happiness was complete as they paused before entering the church and her mother said to her: 'Here, my daughter, you shall hold our baby, you are like a second mother to us all.' Abiodun Olufunmilayo opened her eyes and lay still as Ireti took her into her arms.

## *Friday*

Shifawu couldn't help smiling to herself as she opened her desk and found her books ready for the next lesson. Friday at school was so different from Friday at home. She pictured her family at home for a minute. Her father would be there with his two wives and all the children except herself and Raheem. Her parents were Moslems and they kept strictly to the times of prayer and worship. Five times every day they stopped whatever they were doing for prayer. Friday was the special day when all good Moslems went to the mosque for worship at midday.

Perhaps it was as well that her home was fifteen miles away at Agege. It seemed a long way every morning and evening on the slow train which took over an hour for the journey, but she was glad there was no chance of her father passing her school and discovering how different her Fridays were. Like other Moslem children at Government and Christian schools, Shifawu and her sister Raheem had permission to neglect these special times of prayer when they came in school time. For the great festivals they sometimes had to miss a day's school. Shifawu was in Class 4 now. Next year she would take her school certificate examination. When the festival of Idu-l-Kabir came round next week, Shifawu was wondering whether her father would let her miss it and come to school if she told him how difficult it was to make up the lessons that she missed. He must not suspect the real reason!

Shifawu enjoyed school. She had done well in her primary school in Agege and had pleaded with her father to be sent to the Girls' High School run by the Methodist Church in Lagos. She had come when she was eleven—four years ago. Raheem had followed her two years later. Mr Lawal had given in to his daughter's pleading simply because he knew it to be a good school. He wasn't interested in it being a Christian school—in fact, if he had given this any thought, he would probably not have allowed them to go there.

Shifawu was good at her lessons. She was nearly always in the top three in the end of term exams. She had applied for a Government scholarship and the principal thought she would probably be awarded one. Her father would be pleased—it meant more money to spend on Ali, his only son, who meant more to him than all his daughters. For Shifawu it meant that whatever happened at home she would be able to go on with her studies.

Her favourite subject was Scripture, the next lesson, and one reason why Friday was such a good day. Most of the other children in the school came from Christian homes and had been to Christian primary schools. The Bible stories were familiar to them. In Shifawu's Moslem primary school she had begun most of the other school subjects, and had had lessons from the Koran, the Moslem holy book. They had to recite very long passages all together out loud until they knew most of it by heart. Some of it was beautiful. Some of it didn't seem to make much sense, although she never said so, of course.

When she came as a new girl into Class I she was

curious about this new subject, Scripture. Her curiosity soon gave way to delight. What a wonderful man this Jesus was. She'd been learning about Him for four years now but still could never hear enough about Him. She didn't know, but in the staff room, Miss Green, the European teacher who taught Scripture to her class, often used to say to the other teachers: 'I've never enjoyed teaching Scripture to anyone as much as I do to Shifawu.'

Friday was a good day for another reason too. Lessons were over every day by 1.50 p.m. It was too hot to work after that. Different school societies met for an hour or so after this on most days, ignoring the heat as much as possible. On Fridays it was the turn of the Student Christian Movement.

The S.C.M. meant a great deal to Shifawu. About twenty girls from Classes 4 and 5, the top two classes, met together for an hour or so to pray, read their Bibles, and talk about the Christian faith. Shifawu's best friend, Ruth Olumide, was the secretary of their S.C.M. branch. Once or twice recently Shifawu had stayed for the weekend at Ruth's home in Lagos. Her father was a Methodist minister. He had helped Shifawu to understand the Christian faith. Shifawu had to get permission from her father for these weekends. She told him that it helped her work for Ruth and she to study their books together. This was true, but not the whole truth about the help of these weekends. Besides talking to Ruth's father she was able to go with Ruth to church services on Sunday. She certainly couldn't do that in Agege!

This week at their S.C.M. meeting Ruth's father was coming to speak. He told them all simply and clearly what it meant to follow Jesus Christ, and it seemed to

Shifawu that he was talking directly to her. She thought about his words all the way home in the train. She was sure her father would never understand, though she was not really happy about deceiving him. But so far it had been the only way. Was the time coming when she would have to tell him how she was thinking and feeling? Raheem couldn't quite understand why all this was so important to her elder sister, but she was completely loyal to her and did not say a word at home about Shifawu's great interest in Christianity.

Together they walked from the train to their home. Right in the distance they could see their father standing at the door. As they got nearer they could see his face was full of anger.

He took no notice of Raheem.

'Shifawu, go to my room,' he thundered.

In the little room together Shifawu had never known him so angry. Out it came at once. A distant cousin had visited the home that day from Lagos and had mentioned that one Sunday recently he thought he had seen Shifawu and another girl going into a church at service time.

'Is this true?' Mr Lawal shouted.

Shaifawu had always feared her father's temper; he had brought his children up strictly and often whipped them. But now as she faced her father she realized with surprise that she wasn't frightened at all. Instead she was almost glad that at last he knew and she need not keep things secret any longer.

'Yes,' she answered quietly, 'it is true.' Then she heard herself going on, almost as though it was someone else speaking, for certainly she did not know she was going to say—'I do not wish to be a Moslem any longer, Father, I wish to become a Christian.'

With difficulty her father controlled himself. He was terribly angry, but his voice was quieter.

'You are my first-born child, you are clever, you can bring honour to me, but I would sooner see you dead than have you disgrace me by becoming a Christian. Will you promise me to stop your interest in Christianity, to see no more of your friend Ruth, and to take full part in our great festival next week?'

Still Shifawu was not afraid. She looked at her father and said: 'I am sorry, Father, to make you sad and angry, but nothing that you can say or do will make any difference to my love for Jesus Christ.'

'Very well,' said her father, 'tomorrow you shall go to Oke-Eletu, to stay with your grandmother. You know her power. She will give you medicine to make you an obedient girl again. Now leave me.'

The children did not see much of their grandmother, but many were the tales told of her. She knew all about powerful medicines. People said she could cure dreadful diseases but that sometimes she caused them too. Sometimes people who went to her were never heard of again. Sometimes they went mad. It might be all rumour—or it might not.

Shifawu went to the room which she shared with Raheem and her other sisters. Her mother always let her rest and study a little before she expected help with the evening meal. The room was empty as Shifawu had hoped. She sat on her bed and thought. It was no use expecting her father to change his mind. Suddenly she knew what she must do. The last train of the day back to Lagos left in twenty minutes and she would go on it to Ruth's father. He was the only person who could help. She left no message and was able to slip away from home without being seen. Raheem would guess where she was and they would see each other at school. Her father might well never mention her name again unless she returned a Moslem. Later perhaps her mother might risk her husband's anger and meet her in Lagos.

The train seemed slower than ever for Shifawu and the journey was a mixture of sadness and excitement. At last she was in Lagos again and on her way to her friend's home. The sun had set whilst she was on the train, but the city streets were well lit.

Shifawu knocked on the Olumide's door and Ruth opened it.

'Shifawu!—what is the matter—come in.'

Mr Olumide heard their voices and came out of his office. Shifawu told him all that had happened since they had said good-bye after the S.C.M. meeting. Mr Olumide looked very grave as he listened. Like Shifawu, he doubted whether her father would ever let her go home again and he was saddened as he thought of all that it would cost Shifawu if she really became a Christian.

When she had finished he spoke.

'My name is Bandale, which means 'Come with me home'. This is your home for as long as you need it. Ruth will be glad to have a sister. It is late and you are tired. Tomorrow we will speak further. Both of you go to your rest, and go in peace.'

## *Saturday*

When Lolade woke up in the morning, she knew at once that it was a day she liked especially. Saturday! That meant no school, and a day at home with her parents. The next day would be Sunday, another good day. They would go to church in the morning, and to Sunday school with the other boys and girls of the village in the afternoon. Then Monday, and school again. Lolade had been going to school for a year now, and she loved it. Her mother told her once that when she was a little girl there was no school in their village. The nearest one was forty miles away in the big town of Abeokuta. That was much too far to go. Her father said that first the Church and then the Government had built more and more schools, so that now every boy and girl in the southern part of Nigeria could go to school when they were six.

Lolade soon remembered that this was a special Saturday. Dapo, her eleven-year-old brother, was coming home for the weekend. He had been to the same primary school as Lolade, but last January he had gone away from their village of Iju to a boarding-school at Abeokuta. He did not come home very often, but when he did, what tales he told! There were four hundred boys at his school, and they came from all over Nigeria. Some of them came part of the way by canoe. Others had so far to come that they travelled by aeroplane, and could only afford to go home once a year. Lolade had never been far from Iju and could hardly imagine what his school was like. Dapo said it was a tall white building, and water was brought to it in pipes. That was wonderful enough, but even more wonderful were the switches on the walls which you pressed down when you wanted the light to come on. Lolade had never told anyone yet, but she had made up her mind to work very hard at school, so that she too would be able to go away to a secondary school and learn more and more.

But it was no use lying down day-dreaming. Water had to be fetched from the stream. That was her job on Saturdays. She must also clean the bush lamp and fill it with paraffin, so that the house would be light for Dapo tonight. He would have books to read for his home-work, even though he was away from school for the night. So Lolade got up from the mat where she had been lying in the corner of their little hut. She reached for a long, bright, cotton cloth, and wrapped it round her waist like a skirt. Then she went over to where Taiwo and Kehinde were still sleeping on their mat, covered over by a bright piece of cloth. Seven-year-old Lolade was very fond of her four-year-old twin brothers.

'E k'aro o'—'Good morning'—'Wake up,' she called to them.

They opened their eyes and then jumped up. They liked Saturdays too, for Lolade was at home with them all the day. They all went out of the hut, and saw their mother already busy preparing the yam, to make a really big meal for Dapo when he came home. They were going to have some extra pieces of meat and fish in the stew that day. The children each took two little bananas from a basket near their mother, and then Lolade said, 'Come on. We'll go and fetch water from the stream and I will give you your bath.'

Fetching water was hard work, but Taiwo and Kehinde did not mind if Lolade was going too. While she fetched a big zinc bucket, they went over to where they kept two petrol tins, empty and clean. Balancing them on their heads was easy enough when they were empty. It would not be quite so simple coming home.

Their home was nearly at the end of the village, and they had to go through the forest to get to the stream. The twins did not run about, but walked carefully behind their sister, keeping to the narrow path. On either side there might have been snakes curled up and asleep in the undergrowth.

On one side of the path, there were cocoa trees, with their long shiny leaves and the pods beginning to swell. Later on at harvest-time when the pods were ripe the children would help to break them open, take out the beans and put them into big baskets. The children's father was a cocoa farmer and these were some of his trees. The beans were sold to a firm which took them by sea to England. There they were made into something brown and sweet called 'chocolate', which children liked to eat. Lolade thought it was a very long way for it to go.

Fairly soon the thick trees cleared, and they saw the stream with the water sparkling in the sun. A few yards from the water was a huge tree. At the base of the trunk was a little enclosure, the sides made of palm leaves woven together. Lying untidily on the ground inside the enclosure were some tiny bowls made of baked mud. Taiwo and Kehinde kept as far away from it as they could, and reached up to hold Lolade's hand. They were afraid and Lolade knew why. Each day when she was at school, they came to this place with their cousin, to carry back water for their mother. Their cousin was afraid of the tree and had told the twins that the spirit of the stream lived in it. She said that if they made the spirit angry the water would dry up, and the stream would be of no use to the village. Then there would be no water to drink. The little bowls at the foot of the tree contained presents which the village people had brought to make the spirit happy.

Lolade took tight hold of her little brothers' hands and looked down.

'I'm not frightened any more, when I come near the tree,' she told them, 'and there is no need for you to be. My teacher at school says there is Someone who is greater than the spirit. His name is Jesus, and he loves boys and girls, and our fathers and mothers too. My teacher says that if we start to feel frightened, we are to say "Jesu fe mi", "Jesus loves me". That will remind us that He is our friend and always with us and ready to take care of us.'

She made the twins say the words 'Jesu fe mi, Jesu fe mi' out loud, as they went past the tree. She told them that when they came down next week with their cousin, they were to say it then, and remember what it meant.

They put down the bucket and the cans at the water's edge, and ran into the cool stream. They splashed each other and shouted with excitement at the fun they were having. Then Lolade collected a handful of leaves and rolled them up into a ball. She took hold of Taiwo first, and rubbed him all over for his daily bath. She ducked his head under the water and rubbed his curly hair well. Then it was Kehinde's turn. They did not mind Lolade bathing them. Their cousin was not so gentle. She was always in a hurry and did not let them splash about and play.

A little way downstream there was a sandbank in the middle of the water and several women were kneeling there washing their clothes in the running water. They banged them with stones to get the dirt out. Sometimes Lolade helped her mother do this—but there would not be time today. Lolade called a greeting to the women.

Soon it was time to go back and help their mother. They collected the water to take home, and Lolade lifted a can on to each of the twins' heads. Then she lifted the bucket on to her own head, stood still for a moment to balance it, and they set off. They swayed slightly as they walked, to help to balance their loads. The twins held their cans most of the time, but Lolade did not need to hold her bucket at all. The water splashed over the top a little and trickled down on to their faces, but they did not mind that. It helped to keep them cool, and the twins had no clothes on to get wet. It seemed a long way back and the precious water got heavier and heavier, but at last they were through the forest and in sight of home.

A shining new bicycle was propped against the baked mud walls of their home. Tired as they were they hurried to see who had come to visit them. They put down their water in the shade and ran to the door, stopping to let their eyes get used to the dimness of inside after the glare of the sun outside.

Quickly they went forward and knelt a moment in greeting, for there was Mr Idowu, the catechist of their church. All the children liked Mr Idowu. Sometimes he gave them a ride on the crossbar of his bicycle. He always stopped and spoke to them, when he saw them at play. He came to see them in school, too. He needed his bicycle because he was a very busy man, in charge of four other churches, as well as the one at Iju. Besides that, he had to look after the primary schools in three of those villages. He travelled about a lot to get his work done, and every week he cycled twenty miles to see the only minister in the circuit. The minister was a Nigerian too, whose name was the Reverend Ade Ayorinde.

Today Mr Idowu was not in a hurry. He had heard that Dapo was coming home for the weekend and he had called to say how glad he was. When he had greeted the children, he went on talking to their mother and father. Lolade and the twins stayed quietly to listen.

'You know,' he was saying, 'I should like to see your Dapo become a Methodist minister. He is having opportunities at school that I never had. We need men with education to help our Church.'

Dapo's mother was silent. It was not for her to speak with her husband present. Some other time she would tell Mr Idowu that she too longed and prayed for this and would go on praying.

Their father thought hard and then he said, 'My son is the first of our family to go away to school. I have great hopes for him and for the honour he will bring our family. He could become a doctor or a lawyer or a politician and earn much money and have a big car and become very famous. But the boy shall choose. If he decides to serve the Church and to be a minister I will not stand in his way.'

Lolade listened to every word and her eyes grew

wider and wider with excitement. Could this be Dapo they were talking about? Might her own brother one day be such an important and friendly and fine man as the Reverend Mr Ayorinde, more important even than their own Mr Idowu?

Suddenly she heard a noise that sent all her thoughts away. A roar in the distance! Could it be——? Yes, as she looked from the doorway she saw a cloud of dust way down the road. Hastily saying good-bye to Mr Idowu she caught hold of the twins' hands and together they ran out to meet the lorry. Here at last was the lorry that was bringing their brother to them, their brother who would have so many new and exciting things to tell them, and whose own future held so much that was new and exciting.

LESLIE SCRASE

# DAYS IN THE INDIAN SUN

*Stories of South India*

In gratitude for Karuna Anne
and all the love she brought us

# *About the People*

Like Nigeria, India is a huge country. There are very few countries with more people living in them than there are in India. Many different languages are spoken. Of these, there are fourteen languages that are spoken by large numbers of people. India is divided into states and each state is as large as a whole country in Europe. The Indian stories took place in Andhra Pradesh, which is a large state in the southern half of India.

The largest city in Andhra is two cities. We call them the twin cities. They are called Hyderabad and Secunderabad and they are divided only by a huge reservoir. The stories in this book all took place near Medak, which is a small town, between fifty and sixty miles due north of the twin cities.

In Andhra most people speak one of two languages. The Hindus and most Christians speak Telugu. The Moslems and some Christians speak Urdu. Many people speak both languages. Hindus worship many gods and have statues and images of stone and wood and all kinds of ornamental things. Moslems worship one God, Allah, and have tremendous respect for their founder Muhammad. Both Hindus and Moslems admire Jesus, even when they do not become Christians. We also worship one God, but say that Jesus has given us the best knowledge we can have of God, because if you know Jesus, you know God.

# *How to pronounce the Names*

As in Nigeria, all syllables and letters are sounded and carried smoothly on from one to the next. No one syllable is stressed more than another.

*Jayasheela's Christmas*

| | |
|---|---|
| Jayasheela: | Jay ('ay' as *eye*)—each remaining 'a' as 'u' in s*u*n |
| saree: | sa ('a' as *ah*) |
| tabla: | each 'a' as 'u' in s*u*n |
| Telugu: | Tel-oo-goo |
| Shantamma: | Shant = shan't, except that the 't' should sound almost like 'th'. Each 'a' in 'amma' is like 'u' in s*u*n |
| Papoo: | 'a' as 'u' in s*u*n |
| Dayara: | Day ('ay' as *eye*)—each remaining 'a' as 'u' in s*u*n |
| Ratnamma: | Each 'a' as 'u' in s*u*n |
| Anantha Rao: | Anantha—each 'a' as 'u' in s*u*n. Rao ('ao' as *ow* when you are hurt) |

*Sreeni's Tour*

| | |
|---|---|
| Sreenivasa Rao: | -va (as *var*) -sa (as in s*u*n); Rao ('ao' as *ow* when you are hurt) |
| Venkatapur: | Each 'a' as 'u' in s*u*n; -pur (as *poor*) |
| Bhoopatipuram: | Try to squeeze the 'B' and the 'h' together. Each 'a' as 'u' in s*u*n; -pur (as *poor*) |
| Boorakatha: | Each 'a' as 'u' in s*u*n; 'th' is half-way between our 'th' and our 'tt'. It is sounded with the tongue at the back of the top teeth. |
| Shivaiapalli: | Shiv (as in *shiv*er) -ai (as *eye*) -a (as 'u' in s*u*n) -palli (the 'a' as 'u' in s*u*n) |

*Two Easters in the life of Yesudass*

Yesudass: Ye (as in the old English *ye*a) -su (as *soo*) -dass (the 'a' as 'u' in s*u*n)

Abraham: Each 'a' as 'u' in s*u*n

*Mariamma, Barnabas and the Robber*

Mariamma: Each 'a' as 'u' in s*u*n

Barnabas: Bar (as *bar*) -nabas (each 'a' as 'u' in s*u*n) and do not pronounce the 's'

Muthiakota: Mu (a short *moo*) -thi ('i' as *eye*) -a (as 'u' in s*u*n) -ko ('o' as *oh*) -ta ('t' is almost 'th' and 'a' is as 'u' in s*u*n)

Christudass: Christ (as in *Christ*mas) -u (as *oo*) -dass (the 'a' as 'u' in s*u*n)

*Rozina of Mandapuram*

Rozina: Ro (as in *ro*wing a boat) -zi (as *zee*) -na ('a' as 'u' in s*u*n)

Mandapuram: Mand—'ma' (as 'Mo' for *Mo*ther) -a (as 'u' in s*u*n) -pur (as *poor*) -am (as *um*)

Paul: 'au' as *ow* when you are hurt

Thadi John: Thadi—'a' as 'ar' in t*ar*

Susheela: Su (as *soo*) -sheela ('a' as 'u' in s*u*n)

Daniel: Dan -i (as *ee*) -el = Dan-ee-el

Simon: Si (as *see*) -mon (as m*oa*n)

*Swamidass of Bhoopatipuram*

Swamidass: Swa ('a' as *ah*) -midass ('i' as in *i*n) -a (as 'u' in s*u*n)

Yentha Prema: Each 'a' as 'u' in s*u*n; Pre (as *pray*)

Jayaraj: raj—'a' (as *ah*) -j (as *z*)

*Raju and the Jathra*

Raju: 'a' (as *ah*) -ju (as *dzu*—try to fit the 'd' and the 'z' together) -u (as *oo*)

Jathra: Ja (as *jar* -thra ('a' as 'u' in s*u*n)

Dudgaom: D (sounded with the tongue at the back of the top teeth) -u (as *oo*) -dgaom ('aom' as *arm*)

Jai Christu: Jai ('ai' as *eye*); Christ (as *Chreest*) -t (amost as *th*) -u (as *oo*)

Jai Devudu: De (as *day*) -vu (amost as *woo*) -du (as *do*—the 'd' sounded with the back of the tongue on the roof of the month)

Godaveri: -a (as *are*) -ver (as in *ver*se) -i (as in b*i*t)

*Karuna's Christmas*

Karuna: Ka (the 'a' as 'u' in s*u*n) -ru (as *roo*) -na (the 'a' as 'u' in s*u*n)

chapatti: Each 'a' as 'u' in s*u*n. -tt (almost as *th*)

# *Jayasheela's Christmas*

Jayasheela was tall and slender with long graceful arms and long, dark-brown hair hanging to her waist in a single pig-tail. Jaya was a nurse. It was November and already she was thinking of Christmas. She felt that it was going to be the busiest and happiest Christmas she had ever known. As she lay on her bed in the Nurses' Home at Medak she thought about the service that she and other nurses were preparing. She thought about Jesus and Mary and Joseph and she fell asleep.

As she slept she dreamed. She could hear the carols that she and her friends had been singing, and the Christmas lyrics too. They seemed very far away. She drifted in and out of her dream and each time the carols and lyrics sounded nearer. Closer and closer they came getting louder and louder all the time. Was she dreaming? She sat up on her bed. She was not dreaming. They were real singers. She looked at the calendar on her wall. It said '24th November'.

'Of course,' she said to herself, as she swung her legs over the side of the bed, 'it will be the children from our High School.'

She remembered that they came carol singing on 24th November each year. By 24th December school was over and all the boarders had gone home, so they sang a month early instead! She tidied her loose hair and straightened her night saree. She opened her door and joined the other nurses who were all on their way to Matron's lovely new house.

The carollers sang in English and in the Telugu language and the nurses joined in. Some boys were playing drums called tabla and others danced. The moon and stars shone brightly high above them in the clear sky. Even the mosquitoes seemed to leave them alone. Before long the carollers were on their way and Jaya ambled slowly back to her room, chatting to her cousin and her friends as she went. Christmas had begun.

The days passed more and more quickly. There was so much to do. On duty she was always busy looking after her patients, keeping the ward straight and tidy, chasing off the monkeys and dogs and goats and hens and even donkeys that strayed into the hospital to try to find food. She didn't mind the goats and hens and donkeys, but the dogs growled and curled back their lips to show all their teeth because they were hungry, and the monkeys chattered and spat, and sometimes got quite nasty. She had a job with the families of the patients too. They came and stayed in and around the hospital while their loved ones were ill. Some of them slept on the floor under the hospital beds and some slept on the beds. Jaya was very patient with them, but had to turn them out of the wards sometimes so that they could be properly cleaned and tidied ready for the doctors to come around. And all the time she had bandages to see to, pills to hand out, temperatures to take, and all the other things that nurses have to do. When she was off duty there were presents to buy, decorations to make, rehearsals to attend, so that the time simply flew by until the Sunday before Christmas.

That Sunday she was off duty. She went to the

great cathedral at half past eight for the morning carol service in her own language of Telugu. It was a long service, but she didn't mind that. She listened to the story of Christmas and enjoyed singing all the hymns and lyrics, but the most wonderful moment for her was the offering. The stewards came round the congregation for the gifts and then went forward to hand them to the minister. As they walked forward one or two people joined them. One was a poor young woman from a nearby village. Her name was Shantamma. She had been very ill with tuberculosis and Jaya had cared for her. Now she was better. She walked forward with the stewards.

The minister bent down and asked, 'Why have you come forward?'

'I was ill, sir,' said Shantamma, 'and God has made me well in the hospital. I have brought my gift to say "thank-you" to God.'

The minister told all the people why she was making her gift so that they could all be happy with her. Nobody was happier than Jaya. She said, 'Thank you Jesus for letting me help to make her well,' but she said it so quietly that nobody round about heard her.

In the evening Jaya was back in the cathedral, but this time she was in the choir. The service was in English and she and her friends had practised hard with their English choirmaster. They sang one or two carols on their own. The service was not a long one and afterwards Jaya went with her cousin and her friends back to the Nurses' Home. They went straight to the dining hall. At the entrance they kicked off their sandals and washed their right hands. Then they sat down in a circle on the floor, crossing their legs close in front of them, with their knees almost touching the ground. One of the hospital servants brought round the plates, made of leaves sewn together, and placed one in front of each of the nurses. Another came with a large bowl of rice and ladled it out until there was a big pile on each plate. Others came with the curry and curds and papoo.* Matron said 'grace' and the nurses got busy with their right hands, mixing the curry and the rice together into firm little balls, lifting them on their finger ends, and delicately putting them into their mouths with their thumbs. They drank water from glasses, but their lips never touched the glasses. They poured the water into their mouths. They ate and chatted and laughed until their curry was finished, and then they had a banana for pudding. They washed their hands again, slipped on their sandals, then left to get ready to go out.

When they were all ready, they met some of the nursing sisters from the hospital bungalow and set off out of the hospital compound towards a neighbouring village called Dayara. It was a lovely walk along the sandy bullock-cart track in the darkness, with the moon and stars to light the way. Before very long they came to a small hall. At the door they kicked off their sandals and they went inside with bare feet. Inside was a very simple little church. The walls were white-washed; the floor was of sun-baked mud smoothed over with cow dung. The congregation was already there and was already singing, led by Ratnamma the carpenter's wife. Anantha Rao and some of the other men among the nurses had brought some musical instruments and soon the singing was going with a really good swing. For a time they sat cross-legged on the floor and sang. At last, when everybody was ready,

* Papoo is a kind of highly flavoured lentil soup.

the nurses began the evening service. It was very simple, and everybody joined in, until it was time for the sermon. Instead of a sermon the nurses acted the Christmas story. As some of them acted, others of them read from the Bible and Jaya sang two Christmas songs. Her voice rose and fell, climbed high into the sky to join the angels and slipped down and down like a bird to the earth to join Mary and Joseph and the baby Jesus in the stable. Jaya sang beautifully and went to bed very late and very happy that night.

The next morning Jaya was back on duty. She had all her ordinary work to do but she was also busy decorating the ward. She and her cousin, who was also called Jayasheela, were determined that their ward should be the loveliest of them all. Those patients who could helped in the work and soon there were paper chains hanging across the ward and clever designs (in reds and yellows and silver and gold) covering the walls. The electric lights were soon hidden in a mass of glittering tinsel, and over the ward doors in large lettering you could read, 'Welcome', 'Merry Christmas', and similar greetings. From time to time Jaya slipped away from her own ward to have a look at the decorations in other wards. When she was caught peeping she was shooed quickly away. At last the decorating was finished. The two Jayas, and the other nurses in their ward, stopped to look. Little faults were corrected until Sister was perfectly satisfied.

'I'm sure that ours will be the best ward of all this year,' Sister said.

One evening many people came to the hospital for a Christmas Dinner. Afterwards they joined the patients in a large open space in the hospital to see the concert which the nurses were going to give. There were choruses and there were short plays. There was one which showed the doctor doing an operation, but instead of having all his ordinary instruments he used hammers and chisels and saws and choppers! It looked as if he sawed the 'patient's' tummy open and then he took all sorts of things out of the tummy. The audience laughed and laughed until their sides ached. All the funny things that happen in hospitals were shown, and then Tilaka came on to the stage. Tilaka was one of the nurses who was very good at imitations. She imitated one of the doctors and some of the missionaries. She copied them perfectly and they joined in the laughter just as much as anybody else. At last it was Jaya's turn. Music began to play and three or four nurses danced on to the stage. From off stage Jaya began to sing. As her song got going she too danced on to the stage, right into the centre. Soon, all eyes were upon her. Her eyes and head and shoulders, and long, slender arms; her whole body began to sway until every tinest part of her was caught up into the music. Right to her finger tips she was dancing, dancing and singing, singing and dancing. Out in the audience beneath the lovely moon and stars you could have heard a pin drop. There wasn't a sound until she sank into her final restful position and until her voice trembled away into silence. Then, suddenly, the silence was broken as the clapping began. One more part of Jaya's Christmas was over.

On Christmas Eve she was taking part in something very different. This was in the cathedral. One of the missionaries had written a play and Jaya was in it. She was on duty all through the day and there had been a lot to do. Just as she was going off duty Sister called to her.

'I'm afraid that you can't go yet Jaya. A woman

has just been brought to the hospital. She is very ill. We must see to her at once.'

Just for one moment Jaya thought, 'But what about the play?', and then the play was forgotten as she got down to work. She and her friends worked hard and at last they knew that the woman was going to be safe and that she would get better.

'Now,' thought Jaya, 'I've just got time to get ready for the play.'

But, again, just as she was going, Sister called.

'Jaya, what a day this is. Another woman has just arrived. You'll have to help. I'm sorry.'

Jaya's face showed her disappointment, but she got down to work again. The minutes ticked by, but the play was forgotten again as she and her friends struggled to bring this young woman out of danger.

Meanwhile, in the cathedral, all was ready. People were beginning to come. Those who were in the play were beginning to arrive. The play was in Indian dress so that they only had to be made up. As the minutes ticked by the producer began to get worried.

'Where are those nurses?' he kept saying. 'For goodness sake, go and tell them to hurry up', he said at last and sent for them. He didn't know what was going on at the hospital. Still the minutes ticked by. The evening began with a hymn and a prayer. Still the nurses had not arrived.

'Goodness knows how we shall get through', said the producer, nearly frantic by this time, 'but we shall have to start. We can't wait any longer.'

The play began with nearly half of the people who were in it missing. As it began, away in the hospital, there was a sigh of relief from all the nurses. Their patient was out of danger. She too would get well again.

The Sister in charge turned to the nurses. Quietly she said, 'Off you go; quickly. I hope that the play goes well.'

Silently they slipped out while she and the doctor continued with their work. They hurried along the paths to the cathedral, came quietly in through a side entrance, taking off their nurses' caps as they came. Almost unnoticed they took their places filling up the gaps. They were just in time. The producer offered a little 'thank you' prayer to God, and the play continued to tell the story of the coming of Jesus to Bethlehem. Jaya had just got her breath back when she heard the drums and the cymbals and the handshakers beginning their music. Quietly she raised her head and began to sing. Her voice rang throughout the vast spaces of the cathedral, and echoed and re-echoed in every corner, as she sang of her love for the baby Jesus who was born. As she sang all the people felt that they loved Jesus too.

There was very little sleep that night, what with thinking about the play, and getting up for one group of carol singers after another, and then they themselves sang in the wards, and then it was time to go to the cathedral for the Christmas morning service.

What a service that was! People came from miles around. Christians came and people of other religions came too. People who worshipped all the gods of Hinduism came; Moslems came; gypsies came. They came in a constant stream, crowding into the cathedral and filling it. There was never-ending coming and going, and all the time the Christians kept up their singing and praying and reading from the Bible and speaking of Jesus. As people came they brought gifts. Like the shepherds and the wise men, they wanted to bring their gifts to Jesus. At the front of the cathedral was a large crib with a doll to represent Jesus. The people came and laid their gifts by the crib.

When the service was over the nurses hurried back to the hospital and went to their wards. Quickly and carefully they checked over their decorations to make sure that they were just right. Before long the bishop and his wife arrived with a group of their friends, other ministers and their wives. Slowly they made their way round the hospital, praising the work of the nurses and patients and making notes as they went. When they had been all round the hospital they sat down to decide which ward was the best of them all. I wonder if you can guess which it was? Yes, of course, it was Jaya's ward! She and her cousin and their friends were so happy. Their happiness continued all day as they gave their presents and received others. As Jaya lay down on her bed that night, tired out, she only had time to think, 'This really has been the happiest Christmas ever', before she was fast asleep.

# *Sreeni's Tour*

Sreenivasa Rao was a young man. He was studying at the Medak Bible School. The time had come for their February tour. Sreeni and his friends loaded up the bullock cart with rice and vegetables until it was piled high. They put their cooking vessels on as well and finally their rolled-up bedding and clothes. They stood around the bullock cart and prayed for God's blessing, and then they began their journey. The driver prodded his bullocks in the haunches and they lumbered slowly off, with the cart groaning at every turn of the big wheels. Sreeni and his friends walked with it, singing and laughing and chatting as they walked. One of them played a mouth-organ. It was not many miles to the village of Venkatapur and the path was quite a good one. They had started early, before it became too hot, and they arrived in good time to settle into the empty house that was to be their home for a week, and to cook their midday meal.

It was not until the middle of the week that the new missionary joined them. Sreeni had been looking forward to his arrival and was one of the first to welcome him as he cycled into the village—but it was sad news with which he was welcomed. A little baby in the village had died. Sreeni took the missionary with him to the home of the child. Outside the house, Sreeni's friends were all singing Christian songs to help to comfort the family. At the entrance to the house the missionary stopped. It was a small, dark house made of sun-baked mud with a roof thatched with branches and leaves.

The missionary said, 'Please may I come in?'

'Yes, come in', was the answer from inside.

He slipped off his sandals and Sreeni did the same. Then he bent low beneath the overhanging roof and entered the house through the open doorway. Inside, he stood for a moment until his eyes had grown used to the darkness. There were quite a number of people inside, most of them crying quietly. In the centre, wrapped in a white cloth, lay the baby. By its head incense sticks were smouldering giving off their pleasant smell. The mother was rocking to and fro, crying, flicking off any flies which came too near to her child.

Sreeni helped the missionary to talk to the mother and the father. Sreeni could speak English as well as Telugu. The missionary did not speak Telugu very well. After they had spoken to each other for a time, the parents asked if they could have the funeral service. Sreeni's friends led the singing, Sreeni took the prayers and read some of God's kind words from the Bible. Then they all came out of the house, the mother carrying her baby. Outside in the hot sun the father fetched two empty petrol tins. Each of them had one end and one side missing. Gently he took his small daughter from his wife and laid her in one of the tins. Then he fitted the other tin carefully on to the first so that his baby had a little coffin. He raised the coffin and placed it on his head and followed the missionary and Sreeni out to the edge of the village to a small piece of spare ground. There his baby was to be buried. As they walked, Sreeni's friends sang Christian hymns to comfort those who were sad. When they came to the spot where the baby was to be buried, they placed the coffin in the ground and laid flowers on it.

At once there was a terrible wailing. Many people were there who were not Christians. They did not know that the baby was safe with Jesus. They made a a terrible moaning and wailing. The missionary asked Sreeni to tell them all to be quiet. Soon there was absolute silence. The missionary began to talk to them. He spoke in English and Sreeni repeated what he said in Telugu. He told the people about Jesus and how Jesus died and conquered death. He told the people that Jesus had promised that those who loved him would be with him in Heaven after they died. He told them that the baby they had buried was with Jesus and was happy.

'One day', he said, 'you too will die and go to Jesus. Then you will see your baby again and you will also be happy.'

Quietly, Sreeni's friends began to sing again and the people started back to their homes and to their work. Sreeni and the missionary returned to the house where they were staying.

After their midday meal, in the hottest part of the day, the missionary sat with Sreeni and his friends in the house and they talked over the work they were going to do during the next few days. They were working in four villages and for this they had divided into four groups. That night Sreeni's group was to go to Bhoopatipuram. They had an early evening meal and set out at about seven o'clock. They passed the baby's grave and began to walk on the narrow little walls which had been patted up between the rice fields.

Sreeni was in front carrying a petrolmax lantern. It gave out a fiercely bright light and hissed noisily. Next came the missionary and then some more of Sreeni's friends. One of them carried a lantern and the rest carried drums and other instruments, as well as plenty of cheap books about Jesus which could be sold.

They crisscrossed between the rice fields until the missionary had lost all sense of direction. He was so busy watching his feet to make sure that he didn't fall off the little walls that he had no idea where he was going, but Sreeni knew. He and his friends were as sure-footed as goats and they were weaving their way across the rice-fields to a large tree. Here, they joined the path which would lead them to Bhoopatipuram. Once they were on the path, walking was easy and pleasant. The sand was soft to Sreeni's feet, and still warm from the sun. The moon was bright and stars filled the sky. The missionary pointed out the north star and explained how you could always find it by studying the 'plough'. They were on the edge of the forest now. There were not many trees though. The ground was mostly bare rock or bare rough earth with ragged bushes growing untidily. The little group had walked about three miles when it divided into two. One half was going to a village of shepherds who lived under the hill, while Sreeni and the missionary and a couple of others went on to Bhoopatipuram. After another two miles or less, they arrived.

They went through the village and to the people who came out in curiosity they explained why they had come and what they were going to do. They came to a piece of open ground and sat down. There they began to play the drums and cymbals and hand-shakers, and they began to sing. Soon, a small group of children had gathered and they taught them songs. Then more and more people began to come until at last when a large crowd had formed, Sreeni and two of his friends slipped behind a house for a few minutes. When they reappeared they were all dressed up in bright clothes. Two of them had drums hanging round their necks. They stood on a large stretch of bare rock with the petrolmax lighting them up and the moon shining down on them. They began to do a Boorakatha. One of them started to tell a Bible story alternating between song and speaking. Another kept on interrupting and asking questions. And all the time they both told jokes. The one in the middle just looked from one to the other with his mouth wide open, and all he said was, 'Oh,' 'Ah', 'Ay', 'Ooh', 'Aaah', and meaningless grunts like that. The story went on and on and on far into the night telling the village people about Jesus. When finally it was all over the villagers went home, and Sreeni and his group went back the way they had come. They got to bed well after two o'clock in the morning.

The next day the missionary had a walk around the village in which they were staying. Behind their house there was an open gutter. It ran for about fifty yards down one of the paths. It was filthy. The water ran from one pool to the next and over each pool there was a cloud of mosquitoes. The missionary knew that it was one of the worst things to make people ill. He came back to the house and told Sreeni and the others about it.

'I want a spade', he said, 'so that I can dig the gutter until the water runs quickly from top to bottom. Then it will clear away the dirt and stay clear and clean.'

'But YOU can't do that work', said JayaRaj. 'That is work for coolies, not for YOU.'

'I can do whatever work I think I should do,' said the

missionary, 'because I am a Christian. Hindus cannot do whatever work they like, but Christians can.'

'Then I will help', said Jaya straight away.

'And so will I', said Sreeni.

'And I', 'and I', 'and I' came a chorus of voices.

Soon they all had picks and spades and they were busy at work. They worked in the filthy, black ooze, and they dug deeply until every part of that gutter was clean. They ran water from the top until it ran fast and clear from top to bottom. At the bottom they dug out a pit, and this they filled with old bricks collected from all over the village. The water ran into the pit and then disappeared into the ground. People from the village sat and watched this strange sight. What would these Christians do next, they wondered. Jaya explained why they were doing it.

'Now that we have made it clean,' he said, 'you must keep it clean so that you can be healthy and strong like us.'

He felt proud that he was a Christian—and rather tired too.

That night Sreeni went to the village of the shepherds under the hill and he and his friends did the Boorakatha again.

When he got home and slid beneath his blanket on the floor he found that he couldn't go to sleep. The next night was his big night. It was the night that he had been waiting for. It was the night when he was to go to Shivaiapalli. Before he was born his grandfather had gone to Shivaiapalli. He was one of the first Christians to go there. He went and told the people about Jesus, but they didn't want to hear about Him. They only wanted to hear about Shiva, one of their own gods. Their village was named after Shiva. But Sreeni's grandfather continued to tell them about

Jesus, explaining at the same time that Shiva was not a god at all really. When they heard this they grew very angry and they attacked Sreeni's grandfather so fiercely that they killed him.

When Sreeni was a boy, he and his family had lived in the house in Venkatapur where he lay awake now. His father had looked after some of the village Christians in the area and he too had gone to Shivaiapalli. He had gone many times and had told the people about Jesus. They were not pleased, but at least they did not kill him. The next night Sreeni was going to Shivaiapalli. His turn had come.

And so it was that the next night he led the little group across the rice fields and on to a different path. They walked about four miles to a village with a large square right in the middle of it. They put up their books ready for sale and Sreeni's friends began to sing. Sreeni was nowhere to be seen. He had gone off, on his own, to every house in the village in turn telling the villagers that he wanted to speak to them. Soon they began to come, first the children, then their parents. At last about four hundred people had gathered. The missionary was amazed. Sreeni fitted up a projector and a screen, using his petrolmax lantern to light the coloured pictures he had brought. With the pictures he told the story of Jesus.

'Wicked men killed Jesus,' he said, 'as wicked men in this village killed my grandfather. But Jesus is stronger than death. He rose from death and is alive again. He has given life to my grandfather, and he is in heaven. He has given courage to me to speak to you. He wants me to tell you that he loves you and wants you to become Christians.'

When Sreeni had finished most of the people went

straight home, but a few stayed to ask questions and to talk. Some of those who had stayed bought books so that they could learn more about Jesus. Sreeni had wished that some of the people would decide to become Christians that night, and when this did not happen he was a bit disappointed, but the missionary said, 'You have planted good seed tonight and you have planted it well. God will make it grow and one day there will be a harvest. Thank God for allowing you to plant the seed, and do not be disappointed.'

The next day was a Sunday, and the last day of all. In the morning they had a service at the small church in Venkatapur. This was part of the house where they were staying. Then they went around the village visiting all the houses of the Christians and telling them about the special service that night. They also visited the sick and comforted the sad. The church was not nearly big enough for the service in the evening but in the centre of Venkatapur there was a place where two paths crossed. Just here the last monsoon rains had broken down some of the houses. It had made quite a large space and it was just right for the evening's events. First of all Sreeni and Jaya and some of the others got together and began to play and sing. Gradually the people came. The Christians sat on the ground in the centre. People who were not Christians sat all around, some on the ground and some on the broken-down walls of the houses. When quite a big crowd had gathered, the missionary began the evening service. Sreeni and his friends took part, some of them reading from the Bible and others taking the prayers. Then the missionary talked to the people in their own language. He had prepared what he was going to say very carefully. It was very simple and very short. He told the people that Jesus loved them. Because Jesus loved them he came down from heaven and lived on earth for them, he said. Then he told them of the death of Jesus on the Cross.

'We remember his love and his death in a service we call Holy Communion', said the missionary. 'At this service we eat bread and drink wine together. The bread reminds us of the body of Jesus and the wine reminds us of the blood of Jesus. As they are given to us we remember that Jesus gave his life for us so that we could become God's people. He gave his life for everybody because he wanted all of us to be God's people.'

Then the missionary went to a bare rock which was covered with two white cloths. He lifted the top cloth and people could see a small silver plate with pieces of bread on it, and a small silver wine cup with wine in it. The Christians all knelt on the sandy ground and prayed and all the other people watched. Then the missionary took a piece of bread and ate it and prayed. He sipped a little wine from the cup and prayed again. When he had done this he stood up and called the Christians to come. Some of them came forward and knelt in a line in the sand. The missionary took them bread and then he took them wine. They went back to their places and another line of Christians came forward—every single Christian had come forward now. As the missionary began to take the bread along the line there was a movement in the crowd. An old man who was not a Christian stepped forward. Sreeni wondered what he was going to do. Was he going to cause trouble? The old man came forward slowly, and with great difficulty knelt down at the end of the line. A ripple of murmuring ran through the crowd. Sreeni wondered what the missionary would do. Slowly he came along the line, giving a piece of bread to each person. At last he came to the old man. There was a hush in the crowd's murmuring. The missionary gave the old man a piece of bread and told him to eat in memory of Jesus who loved him. Then he took round the wine and he gave this to the old man as well.

'How wonderful,' thought Sreeni, 'tonight, that old man has found that Jesus loves him. I'm glad that I'm a Christian.'

The tour ended that night, and the next morning they went back to the Bible School, but Sreeni will never forget—and neither will the missionary.

## *Two Easters in the Life of Yesudass*

The parents of Yesudass were not Christians. They were Hindus and they worshipped many gods. For many years they had prayed to their gods for a son, but no son was born to them. Some Christian friends told them about Jesus, and said, 'Why don't you ask Jesus for a son? He is the only real God and he is the only person who can give you a son. If it is right for you to have a son, he will give you one. You pray to Jesus.'

They did as their friends suggested and before very long Yesudass was born.

The parents of Yesudass were not Christians. They did not intend to become Christians, but they knew that it was Jesus who had given them their son.

'We are not Christians but our son must be a Christian. Jesus gave him to us and we must give him to Jesus,' they said.

They gave him a 'Christian' name, for the name 'Yesudass' means 'servant of Yesu' and 'Yesu' means 'Jesus'.

'He has a Christian name,' said his father. 'Now he must have a Christian haircut.'

Yes, that is what he said, 'a Christian haircut'. You see, it is a custom amongst the Hindus to take their sons to a priest for their first haircut, so the parents of Yesudass naturally thought that they must take their son to a Christian 'priest' for his first haircut.

Their friends told them to wait until Easter.

'At Easter we shall have a big service. The bishop is coming,' they said. 'There will be baptisms and confirmations. There will be singing and sermons and those who are full members will be eating the supper of the Lord Jesus.'

The parents of Yesudass didn't understand what they were talking about.

'What are baptisms and confirmations and what is the supper of the Lord Jesus?' they asked.

Their friends tried to explain and Yesudass' parents thought that their son ought to be baptized as well as having a Christian haircut. They waited impatiently for Easter.

At last it was Easter-time and the great day dawned when the bishop was coming. People from five villages gathered together in a large grove of mango trees decorated with coloured flags. At one end an archway had been set up with a big notice saying 'Welcome', and at the other end was a communion table covered with a lovely white cloth. There were hundreds of people all waiting for the bishop.

At about two o'clock in the afternoon they saw the bishop's jeep lurching from side to side as it came down the bullock cart track to the other side of the river. Some of the people were there to meet the bishop, his wife and his friends. They put garlands of flowers around their necks. Two men carried the bishop's wife across the river while the rest waded. A small band struck up. There were two or three buglers, two or three drummers with drums like gongs, and there was a man with bagpipes. The drummers danced as they played, and then they called for a coin. The bishop threw a coin on to the ground and one of the drummers bent lower and lower, playing all the time. Down and down he went until his forehead rested on the coin. Then up and up he came, still drumming all the time, and the coin was sticking to the perspiration on his forehead. He tossed it into the air, caught it, and asked for another. Slowly the procession advanced, the band in front, then the bishop and his friends, and then all the people. They went under the archway with the notice saying 'Welcome' and settled down for the big service.

One of the first things that happened, happened to Yesudass. His parents brought him to the bishop and told the bishop about him, how they had prayed to Jesus for him and how they wanted to give him to Jesus. They asked the bishop to give him his first haircut, and this he did. Then they asked the bishop to baptize him.

The bishop said, 'Are you Christians?'

'No', they answered.

'Then I am very sorry, but I cannot baptize your son. You see, when a baby is baptized his parents have to make some promises to God. They cannot make these promises unless they are Christians. Your son will have to wait until he is grown up. Then he will be able to make his own promises and we shall be able to baptize him.'

The parents of Yesudass looked very, very sad.

'Stay and watch the service this afternoon,' said the bishop gently. 'Maybe Jesus is saying to you, "I want you as well as your son". If he is, then we shall teach you all about him and when you are ready we shall baptize you and make you Christians. Your son could be baptized then.'

They thanked him, and went and sat amongst all the people. As the people sang they wished that they knew the Christian songs so that they could join in. They did join in the prayers, and they listened to the Bible and to the bishop's talk. He showed them some pictures and explained them simply. Then he led them all down to the river. Two of the ministers went into the river and the bishop prayed. Then mothers brought their babies into the water and the two ministers baptized them. The parents of Yesudass wished that they were allowed to bring their son. Then some young men went into the water and knelt down. One of the ministers placed his hand on their heads, one by one. Gently, he ducked them under the water, once, twice, three times, in the name of the Father and of the Son and of the Holy Spirit.

The parents of Yesudass thought, 'That is what our son will have to do when he is older.'

Next some grown-up people went into the water and they were also baptized. Last of all, an old, old man went down into the water. He was given the name Abraham. As the parents of Yesudass watched these full-grown men and women being baptized and as they saw how happy they all were, they felt a deep longing in their hearts. For the very first time they wished that they could be Christians too, but they were far too shy to tell anybody. When the service was all over and the bishop had gone, they went back to their village with Yesudass and settled down to their ordinary life again. They worked in the fields, growing rice and maize and sugar. They looked after their little house, but most of all they looked after Yesudass.

One day a Christian minister came to their village. In the evening he visited all the houses of the Christians. The parents of Yesudass saw the lanterns bobbing about as he went from house to house. They heard the sound of the drums and the voices of the people as they sang hymns and prayed in the houses. Once more they felt that they would like to be Christians so that they could sing those songs and so that the minister would come to their house and pray. They watched the lanterns go from house to house. They seemed to be coming nearer. They *were* coming nearer. Where could they be going? No Christians lived near Yesudass and his parents.

Suddenly his father said, 'They are coming here! Quick, fetch the best mat. Bring it out for them to sit on.'

Yesudass' mother rushed into the house and brought out her best mat and laid it on the open part of their house. The minister came and kicked off his sandals, and those who were with him did the same.

The minister raised his hands in front of his face and placed them together as we do to pray, and he said, 'Namascārum', which means 'How do you do.' Then he said, 'May I come in?'

The father and mother of Yesudass raised their hands, and the father said, 'How do you do. Please come in and sit down.'

The minister entered the open part of their little house and sat cross-legged on the mat, and those who were with him also sat down. The minister put a big Bible on the mat in front of him and then he said, 'We have come to have a look at Yesudass. Is he well?'

'Yes, he is well', they said, and they lifted Yesudass out from an inner room and placed him on the mat for all to see him.

'He is a fine lad', said the minister. 'Did you enjoy the big service on the day when the bishop came and when Yesudass had his first hair-cut?'

'Oh yes,' replied the boy's father. 'We enjoyed it very much. We have talked of it ever since. We have sometimes said that . . .' and he suddenly looked very shy and embarrassed and his voice tailed off into silence.

The minister smiled and continued the sentence that had never been finished, 'that you would like to know more about Jesus?'

'Yes,' said the father of Yesudass, looking at his feet.

'Listen then', the minister said. 'First of all we are going to sing a song about the love of Jesus.'

He started to sing and the other Christians joined in. Every verse had a simple chorus and soon the parents of Yesudass found themselves able to join in.

'Now I am going to read to you from God's book', the minister told them, and he read one of the stories of Jesus.

'Did you understand that story?' he asked. ' Let me explain it to you', and he talked about the story.

'Why don't you come with the Christians to their church tonight. We are going to have a service and you will be able to learn more. You could come to prayers every night at the church. Then you would learn a great deal about Jesus. We would be very glad to see you.'

The parents of Yesudass had enjoyed the story of Jesus and they decided to go to the church that night. They enjoyed themselves so much that they went the next night too. The minister wasn't there. They were very surprised to find a young man of their own village standing up before the congregation teaching them. He could read from God's book.

'How did he learn to read?' they asked one of the people in the congregation.

'He went to the next village where we have a Christian teacher and he learned there. Then he went away for some training and now he is our leader. He teaches us. Doesn't he do well?' answered the Christian in the congregation proudly.

'Yes, he does do well,' said Yesudass' father with admiration, and he determined that he too would learn to read.

So began regular nightly visits to the church for prayers, and weekly visits to the next village to learn to read. The parents of Yesudass learned more and more about Jesus. They learned many Christian songs, but somehow they never felt perfectly happy.

Then one day the minister came again, and he visited their house again.

'Sir', said the father of Yesudass, much more bravely than he had done before, 'tell us what we have got to do to become Christians.'

His wife was surprised and very happy for she wanted to be a Christian more than anything else on earth.

'You have some images in your house which remind you of the Hindu gods, and you pray before them. Those must be broken and thrown away. Then you must learn just what it means to be a Christian. When you are ready to tell others that you love Jesus and when you know what it means to be a Christian, we shall baptize you.'

It was hard for the parents of Yesudass to break their old images and to throw them away, but the Christians came and helped them by singing and cheering and praying. Once that was done, they found that it was easy to learn to follow Jesus. They were not afraid of anything now because they knew that Jesus was stronger than their old gods. They felt happier than they had

DG.

ever been. At last they were ready. It was near to Easter-time, and at Easter the bishop was going to come again. They waited impatiently for his coming. On the day of his coming they went with all the Christians from their village to the same large grove of mango trees, decorated with coloured flags. There were people from four other villages there. There was the same big notice saying 'Welcome' and the same Communion table covered with a lovely white cloth.

At about two o'clock in the afternoon they saw the bishop's jeep lurching from side to side as it came down the bullock cart track to the other side of the river. Some of the people were there to meet the bishop, his wife and his friends. They put garlands of flowers around their necks. Two men carried the bishop's wife across the river while the rest waded. A small band struck up. There were two or three buglers, two or three drummers with drums like gongs, and there was a man with bagpipes. Everything happened just as it had happened before, until it was time to go in procession down to the river for the baptisms. Some children were baptized, and then some young men and young women, and then some grown up men and women, and last of all the parents of Yesudass. They remembered how Abraham and Sarah had prayed for a son for a long time and at last had been given a son, and so they chose to be called 'Abraham' and 'Sarah'.

I have said that they were baptized last of all. That is not quite true. After they had been baptized, Sarah hurried to the bank of the river and lifted her young son in her arms, and she and Abraham brought their son to the ministers who had been baptizing the people.

'Sir', they said to one of the ministers, 'last year we brought our son for his first hair-cut and we asked if he could be baptized. The bishop said that he could not be baptized because we were not Christians. Now we have been baptized and we are Christians. We wish our son to be baptized.'

'He shall be baptized', said the minister, whose name was Luke. 'What is his name?'

'Yesudass', they replied.

'That is a good name', said the Reverend Luke (and you will remember that Yesudass means 'Servant of Jesus'). 'May this boy always be a faithful servant of Jesus', and with that he baptized him. Abraham and Sarah felt that that was the happiest moment of their lives.

## *Mariamma, Barnabas and the Robber*

Mariamma looked old, much older that she really was. Her husband had died and she had known much trouble. She had one son called Barnabas. Barnabas had never been to a school. He was a good boy, about ten years old. He worked for a money-lender. The money-lender gave him one good meal every day and about ten shillings a month in wages. Mariamma was terribly poor and she was also very ill. Once a month she used to walk from Muthiakota, where she lived, to Medak. It would have been a pleasant walk if she hadn't been so tired.

First she went through rice fields where her friends were working. The bullock cart track was quite a good one and walking was easy. There were lovely white cattle-egrets in the fields, like white herons, standing erect and still. Similar in size and behaviour was the conga or paddy bird. Resting on the back of a buffalo was a crow, and making a lot of noise was a group of Indian starlings or mynas. A vivid flash of turquoise crossing the path caught everybody's eye. It was the blue jay, though Mariamma called it 'parla-pittha'.

The path climbed a little away from the rice fields and passed some date palms. Earthenware pots were hanging from the trees collecting the sap. Mariamma felt terribly hot and thirsty, for April is almost the hottest time of the year, but she continued to walk steadily on towards Medak. The path grew rougher with great holes and ruts in it but it was easy for a walker to miss these and to trace a good footpath where many feet had gone before. Soon she was passing another village called Dayara. She was always glad to get to Dayara because she could see the Christian compound not far beyond and she knew that she was near to the end of her journey.

She slipped through the narrow stile in the compound wall and went straight to the hospital. There she joined others who were waiting until at last she was taken in to the tall lady doctor. She went every month. There was not much that the doctor could do for her, but what she could do was done, and afterwards Mariamma knew that she would be able to beg a good midday meal at the bungalow where the lady doctor lived with missionary sisters and nurses. After she had eaten, she found a shady place under a tree and she rested. She talked to other people and she dozed and the afternoon slipped by.

Mariamma made her way to the bishop's house and sat down outside his office. She waited patiently while he dealt with many people, but at last it was her turn to see him. He spoke to her kindly and asked after Barnabas. He gave her seven shillings and sixpence and he prayed with her. He did the same every month. She could scrape a living for a week out of that seven shillings and sixpence. Barnabas's money gave her a living for another week. She only had to beg for two to two-and-a-half weeks in the month. She thanked God for his kindness.

That evening Barnabas came into Medak too. He and his mother soon begged an evening meal, for the

Christians were very kind and generous, and most of them knew Mariamma and Barnabas. After they had eaten, they went down to the Bible school and found a quiet spot in one of the empty classrooms, and there they spent the night sleeping soundly.

Most people in Muthiakota were fast asleep too, but there was one who was not asleep. At about midnight a man slipped quietly into the village. He went from house to house, listening carefully with his ear against one wall after another.

At last he came to Mariamma's house. He put his ear to the wall. He couldn't hear a sound. He crept all round the house and listened again and again. Strangely enough he didn't notice that the house was locked up and that the lock was on the outside. That would have told him that there was no one there. He had a good look all round and then began to dig a hole in one wall of the house. He was jumpy and kept stopping and listening, and running away a little, first one way and then another, to see if anyone could hear him. Suddenly his digger broke through the wall. He ran quickly away and waited. His heart was going bang, bang, bang inside him very quickly. Nobody stirred and nobody came. He took a stick and stuck it through the hole and twiddled it about, but there wasn't a sound. He dug some more, making the hole bigger. He wished that he could see inside, but it was much too dark. At last the hole was big enough to crawl through.

Once more he ran hither and thither making quite sure that nobody was stirring, and then he crept into the little two-roomed house. He stopped quite still inside until he was used to the darkness. Some light was coming through the hole he had made and some through cracks around the door. He strained his eyes to see into every corner until, at last, he was quite sure that there was nobody there. He hunted for money, but there was none. He hunted for jewels, but there were none of those either. He looked for other valuables, but there was absolutely nothing. He grew angrier and angrier. He had gone to all that trouble for nothing—well, almost nothing. In the smaller of the two rooms there was a small pile of rice. Mariamma had been storing it very carefully. Folded neatly in another spot were two sarees—the only spare clothes that Mariamma had. Placed side by side were three or four saucepans and cooking vessels. The thief took one of the sarees and opened it up. He poured all the rice on to it. Then he looked at the cooking vessels. They were too old to be worth taking. He took the sarees and the rice and he crawled through the hole in the wall, and away he ran. Nobody knows who he was or where he went. He was never caught.

Early the next morning Mariamma and Barnabas got up and washed carefully. They rolled up their blanket and set off for home. Past Dayara they walked as the sun rose above the horizon; past the date palm trees; along the bullock cart track that ran through the rice fields; and into Muthiakota. They came to their little house and Mariamma unlocked the door. They walked inside and then Mariamma saw what had happened. She screamed and fell to the floor, fainting. Barnabas also saw the hole in the wall and he ran for help. Soon there were many neighbours around the house and many inside. Soon Christudass, the Christian teacher came. He lived in the village and worked amongst the people there as a teacher and preacher. Mariamma was now sitting up, wailing. Other women wailed with her, while the men stood and talked.

When Christudass came the talking stopped and the wailing also stopped. He talked to Mariamma. Then he called one of the other women.

'Shantamma! Give food to Mariamma today.'

Then he turned to the men.

'We will fill up the hole in the wall', he said.

Men and women worked, and they repaired Mariamma's house. Barnabas was proud to be allowed to help. Shantamma took Mariamma to her home and looked after her. That night Christudass slept with others by the door of Mariamma's house, so that she was not afraid. The next morning Barnabas went back to work and the other men and women went back to their normal work.

Christudass came to Mariamma's house again after he had had his breakfast, and he said to her, 'We will go to Medak.'

Together they set off through the rice-fields, past the date palms, past Dayara village and into the Christian compound. They went to see the bishop, but he had gone away on a tour. It would be two weeks before he came again. Mariamma felt that all hope was gone. The bishop would have helped, but nobody else could. Christudass wondered what to do. For a long time he wondered and he thought and he prayed.

At last he said, 'We will go and see my teacher, one of the men who taught me when I was at the Bible school.'

They came to the teacher's house, but he was at the school. They settled down to wait.

Christudass' teacher came home at midday, but Christudass and Mariamma were nowhere to be seen. They were down at the cook's house eating a meal he had prepared for them. After the teacher had eaten they came to see him, for he did not rest. Christudass told him about the thief.

'Tell me all about Mariamma', he said. 'I want to know all about her.'

Christudass told him about her illness, about Barnabas, and then told him again about the thief.

'What did the thief steal?' asked the teacher.

'Two sarees and some rice', Christudass replied.

'How much rice', asked the teacher, and Christudass told him.

The teacher asked them to wait and he went inside and spoke to his wife.

'What do you think we ought to do?' he asked her, when he had told her about Mariamma.

'As much as we possibly can', she answered.

The teacher went into his study and shut the door and he prayed. Then he opened a drawer and took out some money, put it into an envelope and went outside.

'Take Mariamma to the shops in the bazaar', he said to Christudass. 'Buy her two sarees and as much rice as she has lost. Then come back here. I would like to see what you have bought.'

Christudass and Mariamma went shopping and came back, and Mariamma was overjoyed.

'Now', said the teacher, 'I have done my part. I will also do what the bishop does each month. But the Christians in Muthiakota must do their part. Tell them that they are to take it in turns to give one meal a day to Mariamma. Barnabas, the bishop, and I will also give her one meal a day. We cannot make her better but we can save her from starving and we can give her happiness and Christian love.'

Mariamma tried to tell the teacher how thankful she

was to him and to God, and then they prayed together.

The next day Mariamma went back to Muthiakota with Barnabas (who had come to Medak for the night once more) and with Christudass. Christudass told his people what the teacher had said, and they promised to provide a daily meal for Mariamma.

'It's an ill wind that blows nobody any good', thought Christudass who knew some English, but Mariamma just thanked God for all his kindness.

# *Rozina of Mandapuram*

It was seven o'clock on a Sunday morning in June. Three young men came from the Bible School compound on cycles to the home of the new missionary. He had just finished his breakfast and was busy tying a small case on to the back of his cycle. The four of them rode round to the back of the house, out through a small garden gate and through the main gate of the Christian compound on to the main road. They were going to a village called Mandapuram nearly ten miles away. None of them had ever been there before, but they had asked the way and were sure that they would arrive safely.

'Cycle along the old main road to town until you come to the tree with seven branches,' they had been told. 'When you come to that tree, turn left and you'll come to Mandapuram.'

They by-passed Medak town and rode down to the old causeway that ran through the river bed near Medak. The rains had begun and the river was beginning to change from a narrow, gentle little river, running in the midst of a vast expanse of bare rocks, to the great, rushing torrent that it is for a few days in every year, carrying boulders and trees and anything else that stands in its path along with it. On this Sunday it was faster than usual but not very full. The four cyclists climbed the other side and rode along steadily as the sun climbed visibly into the sky bringing warmth and colour everywhere. It shone on small reservoirs and on the vivid greens of rice fields. The new missionary was enchanted with the beauty of his part of India and with the powerful majesty of huge outcrops of rock on the hills, some of them decorated with thick white and ochre stripes showing them to be places of special holiness; but his companions were not convinced that their land was beautiful.

The road took them through scruffy forest areas with short, untidy trees holding their big leaves still in the morning air. As the trees whipped by on either side they wondered how they could possibly find the tree with seven branches. The miles slipped away as they climbed gently out of the bowl of land in which Medak lies. They came to a section of road where the trees move back from the road leaving clear ground on either side, and then as the trees closed upon them once more they saw what they were looking for, as clear as any signpost: the tree with the seven branches. As they drew near, two khaki-clad boys jumped up and greeted them. They had come to take the visitors to their village.

'Hello, what's your name?' said the new missionary to the taller of the two.

'My name is Paul,' said the boy.

'That is a good name to have—and what's yours?' he said turning to the other, stockier lad.

'My name is Paul,' came the reply.

'Two Pauls', said the missionary. 'That's easy to remember anyway', and they set off down the footpath that led through the forest.

The boys were a friendly, cheerful pair and made very good company so that it seemed no distance at all to Mandapuram. They passed through the main village and across a narrow, dirty stream to the poorest part of the village where the Christians lived. Here there was a three-sided church and people were already gathering for the morning service. Thadi John the Christian teacher was there and his wife brought out coffee for the four visitors. They had kicked off their sandals at the entrance to the Church and now sat cross-legged on the ground to drink. The new missionary wasn't very good at this and was glad to go into the house at the back of the church to get ready for the service.

The drums were soon playing and people began to sing as more and more worshippers came. Before long the little church was full and people stood outside. The women and young children sat at the front and the men sat at the back, all of them cross-legged on the floor. The service was very much like our own, except that a number of children and adults were baptized early on and Holy Communion was celebrated at the end. It all took rather a long time but everybody was very happy. Afterwards Thadi John took the visitors around the houses of the Christians and they chatted and prayed in each one. They came to the house of Abraham. It was a typical, small, dark, two-roomed house with a roughly thatched roof. Abraham himself was sick. The new missionary knew nothing about medicine at all, but he knelt beside Abraham and talked to him, and then he talked to the family.

'Has Abraham been ill long?'

'Oh yes, for many weeks.'

'Why have you not brought him to our hospital at Medak?'

'We have no money to pay the hospital bills.'

'You must not worry about the bills. You must bring him to the hospital today. Do you promise that you will bring him?'

'Yes, we will bring him.'

The visitors prayed and then moved on to the next house until they had finished their visiting.

At last they returned to Thadi John's house for a midday meal of curry and rice.

'You will see that they bring Abraham, won't you', said the missionary after their meal was over and when they were almost ready to go.

'I think that they are already on their way. You will pass them on your way home. Will you pray with us before you go?'

They prayed together, thanked Thadi John and his wife for all their kindness and for the lovely meal, and then set off back along the footpath to the main road.

Sure enough, on their way home they passed a bullock cart in which old Abraham was lying. His two sons, their wives, and his grand-daughter Rozina, were with him. The cyclists left them behind and they did not arrive until the evening. They went to the hospital and Abraham was admitted. Susheela, one of his daughters-in-law, and Rozina, his grand-daughter, remained to help look after him in the hospital. They slept beneath his hospital bed by night and they kept him company and cooked his meals by day. The hospital wards were almost always full of the relations of patients. Sometimes it was difficult to tell which were the patients and which were their relations, for sometimes the patients would sleep on the floor and sometimes their relations would sleep on their beds!

Abraham had tuberculosis. He was very ill. He lay in hospital for two weeks and then he died. The new missionary helped to take his funeral, afterwards giving comfort to the grief-stricken family.

The tall, lady doctor said, 'Did you know that Susheela had tuberculosis some time ago? She was a patient of ours and got better.'

'I didn't know,' answered the new missionary. 'Do you think that any other members of the family may have the same illness?'

'It's quite possible,' she replied.

The new missionary went to see the doctor in charge of the hospital, Dr Daniel.

'Doctor, you know Abraham of Mandapuram who died—did you know that his daughter-in-law had had T.B.?'

'Yes,' replied the doctor, 'I knew about her.'

Dr Daniel knew nearly everybody everywhere!

'I wondered if we could have the whole family in for examination,' said the new missionary, 'to find out if any of the others is ill.'

Dr Daniel arranged a day and the new missionary cycled out to Mandapuram with one of his students called Sreenivasa Rao and they made arrangements for the family to come to the hospital. Thadi John made sure that they came.

There were thirteen of them altogether and they were all X-rayed. Simon had brought some papers with him which showed that when he had worked in the city he had fallen ill and gone to one of the city hospitals for treatment. He was well now and so was Susheela. Most of the family was well, but Shantamma and Rozina both had T.B.

'You two must stay in the hospital,' said Dr Daniel.

'But we have no money. How shall we pay the bills?' they answered.

'The new missionary says that you must stay. We will ask him about the bills', and so it was that they stayed.

The new missionary wrote to friends in England and they gave money to pay the bills for Shantamma and Rozina. After three months Shantamma was able to go home, but Rozina had to stay longer.

She was anything between nine and fourteen years old. When she first came to the hospital she looked like a wizened old lady, but little by little her face grew younger. At home she looked after the cattle but in the hospital she played with other girls, she learned to read and write, and she learned many, many stories of Jesus and many Christian songs. She became a firm favourite of the nurses and they were all very kind to her. They brought her special treats; they spent some of their spare time with her; they made her so happy that she didn't mind being away from home too much. Sometimes they had concerts or plays in the hospital and Rozina loved going to those. From time to time the new missionary came to see her. She and the other children always made a big fuss of him and had lots of fun trying to talk to him. He made so many mistakes in their language—it was like talking to a little boy.

At last the day came when Rozina was fit and well. Now she could go home. Her family came from Mandapuram to take her home, and Thadi John and his wife came too. They came on a Sunday and they all went to the cathedral for the morning service. The time came for people to give their offerings. The stewards came around and then went in procession to the communion rail while all the congregation sang. As they walked forward people joined them from different parts of the congregation. Very shyly, Rozina stood

DG

up and walked forward and stood with the stewards. The minister took the gifts from the stewards and placed them on the communion table. Then he began to take gifts from the other people.

'Why have you come?' he asked one woman.

'A cobra curled around my ankle but did not bite me. I have come to thank God,' she answered, and the minister told the congregation.

Then he asked a boy why he had come.

'It's my birthday and I want to thank God for it,' came the reply.

At last he came to Rozina. She handed over a bowl of rice and a coconut and a coin worth about a penny.

'I have come to thank God because I have been ill and he has given us the hospital and doctors and nurses, and I am better,' she said happily.

When the service was over Rozina and her family made their way to the home of the new missionary. They waited until he returned from the village he had gone to that morning. When he returned he called his wife and his children and they stood and talked on the verandah of his house. Rozina's family took necklaces of flowers and hung them around the necks of the missionary and his wife and children, and then Thadi John spoke for them all.

'We have come to thank you,' he said.

'You must not thank me,' said the missionary. 'You must thank God and his doctors and nurses.'

'We do thank Him and we do thank them, but it is through you that Shantamma and Rozina are better.'

'No,' answered the missionary. 'It is your friends in England who have paid your bills. You must thank them, but do not thank me.'

'We thank them too and we pray for them,' replied

Thadi John. 'They have sent their money, but you have come to us. You have shown us that Jesus loves ordinary village people and cares for them.'

While he had been speaking Simon had disappeared. Now he returned with a hen with its legs tied together. He gave it to the wife of the new missionary, who handed it to her cook rather quickly! Then Thadi John's wife drew her hand out of her saree and gave something to her husband. He opened it out and placed it round the neck of the new missionary. It was a lead crucifix on a long black cotton. Then they prayed together before the Mandapuram people set off for home. Rozina felt it had almost been worth being ill. She had had a wonderful six months—and she had a wonderful homecoming.

## *Swamidass of Bhoopatipuram*

Back in February, Sreeni and some of the other students had taken the new missionary to Bhoopatipuram. They had gone by night and gathered a large audience each time they had gone, for the pictures and the boorakatha were both very popular. On one occasion they had gone in the morning to take a Christian service. Very few people came—perhaps twelve adults and twelve children. Sreeni announced the first hymn, one that every Telugu Christian knows, a hymn about the love of Jesus called 'Yentha Prema' ('How much Love').

Nobody sang except Sreeni and his friends.

'Don't you know "Yentha Prema"?'

'No, we don't know it.'

'What hymns do you know?'

'We don't know any hymns.'

'But you are Christians aren't you?'

'We have forgotten all that we ever knew. It is many years since Christian teachers came here,' and an old man began to tell the story of the church in Bhoopatipuram.

He began with the days when Christian preachers first visited the village. He told how a few of them were interested and the preachers came again and again. After a time some of them became Christians. They were baptized and they had their babies baptized.

Then they began to want a church to worship in. They began to gather stones and mud and at last they were ready. Near to their homes was an old Hindu god. It was a bit battered and broken but they were very fond of it so they built their church over the top of it. When the Hindus saw what they were doing they grew very angry, and one day they got together and came to the little Christian church and they pulled it down. A Christian preacher heard what they had done. He came to the village and a great crowd gathered. First he told the Christians that they should not have built their church over the Hindu god. It showed that they were still too fond of their old gods. They should have nothing more to do with them for they were not gods at all. Christians could laugh at these old gods for they had no power. Then he turned to the Hindus who were already growing angry because of the way he talked about their gods. He told them that they were wicked people and that God was angry with them for tearing down his church. He told them that God would punish them. They became more and more angry. They took him and threw him out of their village, and they said, 'If any more Christian preachers come to our village, we shall kill them.'

Shortly afterwards the son of the leader of the Hindus fell ill and died. They thought that this was the punishment of God, and the Christians believed this too—but no more Christian preachers came.

Gradually the Christians forgot all that they had been taught. The children who had been baptized grew up knowing nothing about Jesus. That was how things were when Sreeni and his friends came.

When they had heard the story they said, 'Christian teachers and preachers will come to you again. You will have your own church again. But first you must learn many things about Jesus. You must become proper Christians once more.'

And so they taught them 'Yentha Prema'. When they had sung it quite well, Sreeni prayed and asked them to listen very carefully to the Lord's Prayer because that was a prayer that they would have to learn. Then he read to them from the Bible—he read the story of the five loaves and the two fishes and of the boy who gave them to Jesus. After that they all sang 'Yentha Prema' again.

The new missionary stood up to speak.

'Do any of you children go to school?' he asked.

Three of the twelve, all of them boys, put up their hands.

'Can any of you boys read?' asked the missionary.

One boy, ten to twelve years old, put his hand up.

'Come out here and let me see how well you can read,' said the missionary.

The boy came out to the front and read part of the story of the five loaves and two fishes again. He read very well and the missionary praised him and asked him his name.

'Swamidass,' answered the boy.

'Very well Swamidass, sit down while I tell you a story.'

Then, very simply, the missionary told the story of the five loaves and the two fishes and of the boy who gave everything he had to Jesus.

'All those people were fed because that boy gave his lunch to Jesus,' said the missionary.

'Now Swamidass, I want you to give something to Jesus. I want you to give your reading to Jesus. Will you do that?'

Swamidass blushed and felt a mixture of embarrassment and pride and he said that he would.

'Then come out here again.'

Swamidass stood up and came forward.

'You see this book,' said the missionary. 'It is part of the Christian book which we call the Bible. In this book you can find stories of Jesus. I want you to read the book and I want you to tell the stories to all these people. You will be their teacher!'

Then the missionary turned to another book.

'This is a hymn book,' he said. 'Have a look at this hymn. Read the first verse to the people.' Swamidass began to read, 'Yentha prema . . .'

'Now,' said the missionary, 'Sreeni will teach you another hymn and *you* will be able to make sure that the people do not forget. When we come again we'll see how you are getting on.'

All that had happened back in February. Now it was August. The rains had come. It was hot and sticky and there were masses of insects about at night. Sreeni had noticed that the new missionary had a free Sunday.

'Sir,' he said, 'you are not going to the villages next week?'

'No Sreeni. Mr Israel has given me a Sunday off.'

'Shall we go to Bhoopatipuram, sir?'

At seven o'clock on the following Sunday morning, Sreeni, Jayaraj, and John Wesley came to the house of the new missionary and together they set off on their bikes. They rode out of the compound and across the main road, past the bus depot, and on to a bullock cart track straight away. It was harder work than usual because the track was wet and the sand had become clinging mud. They had slithered and slid forward through a wood, across some open country, and down towards the river. It was much higher and faster than usual. In the middle was a big boulder. The water usually lapped gently against its base but now it was rushing fiercely half way up its sides. The boys didn't hesitate. They waded straight in and through the river and the missionary followed. At the other side of the river they stopped while the boys wrung the water out of their trousers and the missionary took a towel out of his case for all of them to dry their legs.

The path was a rough one from the river onwards. It led over some rugged hills and through the forest. It was only a footpath and often went over bare rock and down narrow passages between the rock. Sometimes they walked and sometimes they had to carry their bikes over their heads. Then they came to a wide valley full of vivid, green rice fields. It was beautiful! Yet the boys hardly seemed to notice. They rode out on to the narrow footpath that led through the fields. On either side of the path there was a drop into the mud and water of the rice fields, but they rode without hesitation. Wobbling a little, the new missionary followed, and he managed not to fall off. Bhoopatipuram lay on the hills on the other side of the fields.

An older preacher called Nathanael was there to meet them. The missionary had asked him to come. They gathered the people together—the same group as before and quite a lot of other people as well. Before the service began Sreeni and Jayaraj and John Wesley got busy with the drums and sang one Christian song after another. The people soon learned the choruses and they joined in. When everybody was ready Nathanael asked them to sing 'Yentha Prema'. Young Swamidass stood up in front of the people and began to sing and they all joined in. The tune had changed a little but all the people knew the hymn right through. Prayers and a Bible reading followed and then they sang the other hymn that they had learned, and after that the missionary stood up and called to Swamidass.

'Have you done the job that I gave you to do?'

'Yes,' said Swamidass, and turning to one of the children he said, 'Tell your story.'

The young lad stood up, folded his arms, looked very serious, and told a story about Jesus.

Then Swamidass turned to another boy and he told a different story. Swamidass went down the line of children and each of them told a different story.

'Well,' said the missionary when the children had finished, 'that's wonderful. You have done far more than I would have believed possible.'

'Just a minute, sir,' said Swamidass, and he called to one of the grown-up men.

He also told a story, and one by one twelve of the grown-ups told their stories.

The missionary was amazed.

'Swamidass,' he said, 'you have done your work as a real Christian teacher should. Nathanael has come to your village today and he will be coming to your village regularly. He will teach you many more things, but you Swamidass must continue your work. I hope that when you are grown up it will be possible for you to be a full-time Christian teacher like Nathanael. You have done well and God will bless you all because of it.'

Then Sreeni taught them another hymn, and after that Nathanael spoke. He spoke wisely and his enthusiasm caught hold of them and held them in wrapt attention. He spoke with plenty of good humour so that there was plenty of laughter as well as seriousness. As he finished he put his arm around the shoulder of Swamidass and said, 'So now God has given you two teachers instead of one. Your name, Swamidass, means "servant of the Lord". You must continue to be a faithful servant. My name means "wisdom" for Nathanael in the Bible was very wise and very godly. We must all work together for the sake of Jesus and his Church.'

The four cyclists who rode back to Medak that day were the happiest people on earth—yes, even happier than the Christians they had left behind in Bhoopatipuram. Happier than Swamidass? Well, perhaps not: he was the happiest of them all.

# *Raju and the Jathra*

It was a very important day in Raju's village because the chairman of the district was coming. There was a band, and people came from other villages, and the church was gay with decorations. The chairman was the Reverend E. P. Yesudass, a fine looking man who had lots of stories for the children. He told them that there was going to be a Jathra at Dudgaom, twenty miles away. He wanted them all to come. He wanted them to send rice for the meals. He wanted them to bring their harvest festival gifts. There would be dramas, boorakathas, big services, bullock cart races, all sorts of things. People were coming from many villages. They must also be sure to come.

They were all very excited by the news and they began to save rice and to send it with other gifts of food to Dudgaom in preparation for the Jathra. When the great day in October came, as many as could possibly go piled their belongings into bullock carts and trundled slowly off. They walked a bit and rode a bit and rested a bit. They stopped and cooked meals by the roadside and the children had a wonderful time playing games with one another. As they drew nearer to Dudgaom they were joined by people from other villages. They knew some of them but others were strangers. More and more people filled the road until there was quite a long line of bullock carts all heading for Dudgaom. They arrived at long last and Raju and his friends went off to explore while their mothers prepared the evening meal.

They saw the school—bigger than any school that they had ever seen. They saw the hospital—the very first hospital that they had ever seen. They saw the church and that was bigger than any church that they had ever seen. They peeped inside, and then they went right inside, and they simply stood and stared. They had never seen anything so beautiful in all their lives. They wandered around other encampments and met other children from other villages. They saw a large stage set up in the open air and wondered what that was for. They saw a huge wooden cross right on the very highest ground and they wondered what that was for. And then they felt hungry and went back to their own camp to find their evening curry waiting for them. They ate quickly because they had heard that things were going to start right afterwards with the grand march round the church.

Raju went with his father to harness up their oxen to their cart. The oxen's horns and sides were gaily painted and the cart was decorated with coloured papers. They rode with many others to join the procession by the church. The bishop was there in his white robes and saffron scarf, carrying his shepherd's crook. The chairman of the district was there looking very fine in his white robes and black scarf. Some other ministers were there as well. Then came the boy scouts and after them the women and children, and last of all the bullock carts. Raju began to count but soon gave it up as a bad job. Right in front was a band. As the band started to play the people started to sing and the procession began to move. They walked around

DG

the church three times. At each corner of the church they stopped; the band stopped and the singing stopped and then someone cried in a loud voice, 'Jai Christu', and everybody shouted, 'Jai Christu'; the voice cried 'Jai Devudu', and everybody shouted, 'Jai Devudu'—'Victory to Christ', 'Victory to God'. This was what they shouted and they felt tremendously excited. Then they sang again; then they shouted again; and so they continued until the procession was over. The bishop raised his arms and prayed in a loud voice, and with that the Jathra had begun.

All the bullock carts lumbered off to the top of the hill to get ready for their mighty race. When everybody was ready, the chairman of the district started them off and away they went clumsily and noisily down over the hill as fast as they could go. The whole hill seemed to shake as they thundered down towards the church. Who would get there first? Raju was shouting his head off as he hung on like grim death while their bullock cart lurched and lunged its way down over the hill. His father was shouting his oxen on, shaking the reins with one hand and prodding the beasts in the buttocks with a sharp stick with the other. Soon half a dozen of them were gaining ground. In the dim light of many fires you could see the clouds of dust rising from the hill. Raju got so excited that he let go his hold and went bouncing about the floor of the bullock cart until he managed to grab hold of a side and haul himself to his feet again. His father never noticed. His feet were firmly fixed apart. The reins were working, the stick was working, his voice was calling, the oxen were getting excited too. Three of them led now. They were getting closer and closer together as they all tried to get to the church first.

Raju's father was in the middle. He must get ahead before the other two boxed him in and forced him to drop back. He was tense with excitement. The sweat glistened on his face. Raju was shrieking, shrieking, shrieking with excitement. The other two carts were closing. They grew closer and closer. Suddenly Raju's father gave a lightning jab into the haunches first of one, then of the other of his beasts, and with each jab a tremendous yell. The whole cart seemed to leap forward. Raju clung to his hold grimly—and then 'Yippee-ee-ee!' They had drawn clear. They were leading. They were pulling away. They were first to the church. Hard on they went. They took the first corner wide but not too wide, the same with the second —another cart tried to squeeze past on the inside and nearly cannoned into them—the third, the fourth, on round and round, and the third time round and they had won! What cheers there were for Raju and his father and their oxen and how proud they were as they came back to their own camp and rubbed their animals down and gave them a good feed.

When the oxen had been properly attended to, Raju and his father were so tired that they went straight to sleep and missed everything else that happened that night.

The following day was full of adventures and they all went down and looked at the great Godaveri river. In the evening, after their meal, they went with other people from their village to where the big stage was set up, taking their harvest gifts with them. There was a wonderful service with hundreds and hundreds of people. The bishop and the chairman of the district each took part of the service and then it was time for the offerings. Village group after village group went forward with their gifts. They carried sackfuls of rice forward, and there were coconuts, and hens, and even sheep and goats. The ministers took these things and gave a handful of sweetened puffed rice back to each person as a sign of God's 'Thank you' and his blessing.

Raju enjoyed the puffed rice. He whispered to one or two of the other boys. As the next village group went forward, four boys slipped out of their places and moved quietly forward to join them and thus they got their second handful of sweetened puffed rice. They did the same with the next, and the next, and were doing very well on puffed rice. They went forward with the next group for handful number five. The chairman of the district was handing it out this time. He let them come forward with bowed heads and outstretched hands. Suddenly he moved. Each of them received a firm clip across the ear! They hurried back to their places feeling that they had had all the puffed rice that they wanted for one night!

When the offerings were over the preacher began to speak, but by this time Raju had snuggled into his mother and fallen fast asleep. He slept right through the rest of the service and didn't wake up until his mother shook him saying, 'There is going to be a drama. Don't you want to watch?'

Sure enough, all the ministers had gone and all the gifts had gone and curtains were drawn across the stage. The curtains opened and children from the school, dressed in brightly coloured clothes began to act an exciting story all about a king called Raju. Young Raju sat and listened and imagined that he was that king. When that drama was over there was another, and another, and a fourth! It was nearly breakfast time when they had all finished, but Raju didn't know anything about breakfast. He fell asleep as soon as he got back to their camp and he dreamed a mixed up dream in which he was King Raju and ate nothing but sweetened puffed rice, and the chairman of the district was his slave, and he was one of the three kings who brought their gifts to Jesus and he gave Jesus a sack of rice as well as gold. It was a muddle, but he was very happy.

When he did wake up he was still too tired to do much, but that night, after their evening meal, he livened up again for there was to be a boorakatha. The minstrels told a wonderful story and Raju roared with laughter at the jokes in it. It was queer really, one minute you'd be laughing till your sides ached, and the next you would be as serious as serious could be. He learned a lot about Jacob and Joseph from that boorakatha.

When it was over all the people made their way to the highest part of the hill and to that huge cross. Raju knew what it was for now because the ladies had done the same thing each night. The wife of the chairman of the district stood with some other ministers' wives at the bottom of the cross and two of them stood on ladders part way up the cross. Then ladies of the women's meetings came from all directions. Each lady had in her hand a little saucer of oil with a taper hanging over the edge. The taper was burning and gave a little light, like a candle. As the ladies came towards the cross they seemed to be long lines of light in the darkness of the night. They came to the foot of the cross, handed over their saucers, and moved gracefully away. The ministers' wives took the saucers and placed them on little platforms all over the cross until the whole cross was alight, lit up by the little saucer candles.

In a clear voice that rang through the night air, the wife of the chairman of the district said, 'Jesus Christ is the Light of the World,' and then all the people prayed.

Raju peeped all round him.

'Aren't there a lot of Christians,' he thought. 'There may not be many in my village, but what a tremendous lot there must be in all the world.'

Then he caught words of the prayer: 'We know, O Father, that Jesus is the Light of the World. He has brought light and laughter to us. As the light of this cross shines over this part of the world, grant that the light of Jesus may shine in the hearts of all men, so that they may become Christians with us, and members of thy family. We ask this through Jesus Christ our Lord, Amen.'

'Amen,' said Raju—and he said it so loudly that he surprised even himself.

His father thought he was being naughty, but his mother understood, and whispered, 'Raju really meant that. He's beginning to learn what it means to be a Christian.'

She felt warm and happy inside—and so did Raju.

# *Karuna's Christmas*

Karuna was a happy girl, full of laughter and gaiety. But when her baby brother was born everything changed. At first everybody was full of congratulations and Karuna and her father and mother were very happy and very proud, but very soon after the baby was born a whisper began to go round the village.

'Have you noticed?' 'Have you seen?' 'There's something strange.' 'There's something different.' 'There's something wrong.' 'That baby's queer.'

In this kind of way the women began to talk. Their children heard them and they began to talk as well. When Karuna was at the well drawing water, a group of them came and started shouting, 'Your baby's queer. Your baby's queer.'

Karuna turned on them pale and angry.

'What did you say?'

She stalked towards them, fierce with anger.

'You dare to say that again,' and she looked so fierce that they all turned and ran away.

As soon as they were out of sight Karuna burst into tears and ran all the way home.

Inside her house she sobbed and sobbed. Her mother guessed why and drew her baby close to her. Her father tried to comfort her and asked what was the matter. At last she calmed down enough to tell him. As she looked at him through her tear laden lashes she noticed that he suddenly seemed much older. She looked at her mother and saw that she was crying quietly. So it was true! That was why her mother hadn't let anybody hold the baby or come too near. She crept over to her mother and kissed her and both of them cried noisily. Her father went out of the house.

After a while she said, 'Show him to me Mummy. It doesn't matter what he is like. He is my brother and I must look after him.'

Slowly, almost hesitating, her mother unwrapped the baby. Karuna gasped and then bit her hand to stop herself from crying out. He was white, not brown as she was. She knew that babies were paler when they were born, but he was white. His hair was white. And there was something strange about his eyes. They were never still. They seemed always to be darting from side to side. She moved to let the shaft of light from the tiny window fall on him. He blinked as if he couldn't bear the light. What a strange colour his eyes were. They seemed almost pink and how weak they were. Karuna felt as if a dark cloud had come down on her life.

As the baby grew she helped to look after him. She nursed him. She carried him around on her hip. She took him with her to church. At first the children were unkind and she had many a fight, but the grown-ups told their children to be quiet and soon they got used to having an albino (or sickly white) baby growing up amongst them. The grown-ups did not get used to the baby though. Karuna's house had always had plenty of visitors, but nobody came now. Her mother had been a great favourite with the women and her father with the men, but her mother was left very much alone now. The men weren't so bad, but father spent much more time at home keeping his lonely wife company, and so it was that he spent less and less time chatting with the men in the evenings. Mother, father and Karuna grew very close to one another, but their sorrow clung to them all and it was very rare that any of them laughed or smiled.

Away in Medak on Christmas morning, the new missionary said 'Good bye' to his wife and children, and set out on his bike alone. Sreeni and Jayaraj and all the others were on holiday and had gone to their homes. The missionary cycled down the main road and across the old causeway where the river was back to its normal narrow width. He climbed the other side into the forest and rode on for three or four more miles until he saw the village he was making for away on the left of him beyond a wide expanse of vivid green rice fields. He cycled on until he came to a cart track. He turned on to the track and rode for some time until he found that the track disappeared. It had been ploughed up and rice was growing where it had been.

'Shall I press on or go back and look for another path,' he wondered.

After a minute or two he decided to go forward. He walked along the little walls between the rice fields, patted up by many hands, and he dragged his bike through the mud at the edge of the fields. Whoops! He slipped, he wobbled, and he fell with a splash. Gosh, the water was cold! Luckily he landed on his feet, but he was wet and muddy nearly up to his knees.

He was glad to get to the other side of those rice fields and to begin riding again. Very soon he came to the village. He stopped at the first house.

'Can you tell me where the Christian church is?'

'Yes, come in. Why, what a mess you're in! Which way did you come?'

'I thought that I was taking a short cut across there, but I'd have done better to have gone a longer way round.'

'You certainly would. Come down the garden. My wife will bring water and you can wash.'

They brought hot water and the missionary washed his face and hands and was about to wash his legs.

'I will do that', said Barnabas (for that was the man's name).

'Oh no, you won't', said the missionary, 'I can wash my own feet, thank you.'

'Jesus washed his disciples' feet, didn't he, and he told us to do the same,' said Barnabas, and the missionary felt ashamed and let Barnabas wash his feet. When he was clean he came back to the house and sat in a deck chair and drank the coffee that was so kindly provided. Then he found that Barnabas's wife had prepared breakfast as well. He dared not admit that he had already had breakfast. He thanked them very much and sat on the floor and ate his chapatti and fried egg. (A chapatti is shaped like a pancake and is made from wheat flour.)

'You *will* stay and have a Christmas dinner with us, won't you?' said Barnabas.

'You have been very kind,' replied the missionary, 'but I think that on Christmas Day I ought to go home and be with my wife and two boys. Forgive me if I do not stay.'

As the two had been sitting chatting, people from the village had come to peep at the missionary—some of them just stood and stared for they had never seen an Englishman before.

After a while the missionary said to Barnabas, 'I would like to go to the homes of the Christians,' and so Barnabas took him from house to house. In between two groups of houses there was a large pit. Behind it there was one house which had had to be built further back because of the pit, but its position isolated it a little from the rest. As the two men moved from house to house, more and more people joined them and walked round with them. Children came up close and touched the missionary. They were walking past the isolated house. A young girl about eight or nine years old was sitting in front of it, working.

'What about that house?' said the missionary.

'We do not go there,' came the reply.

The girl looked up as they passed. She saw the missionary and she stared. She dropped her work and ran out into the path and stared some more. She ran on in front and stared again. The missionary was rather amused. She had obviously never seen an Englishman before. She came close and touched him and then ran away a little. She did this several times. Then she came close and he took her hand in his.

They went on from house to house. In every house they prayed and the missionary told the people that they were going to have a Christmas service. They must get ready and come. Barnabas took him to the church. A woman swept the floor of the church so that it was nice and clean.

The little girl ran home. She burst into the house and told her mother and father.

'There is a white man in the village. He is going to take a service. We must all go to church.'

Her parents had seen missionaries before, but they said nothing. They washed and tidied themselves and got ready for the service. Little Karuna, for of course she was the little girl, insisted on carrying her brother. When they arrived, the missionary understood why Karuna had made such a fuss of him, but he took no more notice of the little boy than he did of any other child.

When the service was over Karuna brought her brother to the missionary. She wanted him to see the missionary and to know that he wasn't the only white person in the world. The missionary felt a big lump in his throat.

'I haven't been to your house, have I?' he said to Karuna.

'No, sir', she answered shyly.

'Then take me there now,' he said.

Proudly she led the way. The missionary and Barnabas followed and most of the congregation followed them. Karuna's father and mother had already walked home, lonely as usual. How surprised they were to see Karuna leading all the people. They came crowding into the tiny space outside the house and the missionary kicked off his sandals and came on to the little porch of their house. Karuna's mother had put down a mat and the missionary sat down.

Barnabas also sat down and the people came as close as they could.

'I would like you to sit down', said the missionary to Karuna's parents, 'and I would like you to sit next to me with your brother,' he said to Karuna. 'Do you remember the story I told you in the church?' he said.

'You told us about the wise men who came to Jesus and brought their gifts to him.'

'Did I tell you what colour they were?'

'No, you didn't', answered Karuna.

'We don't know for sure,' said the missionary, 'but it is very possible that they came from different countries. Some of them may have been a nice brown colour, like you. Others may have been paler, like me. God loves people whatever colour they are. He loves dark people and he loves pale people; he loves brown people and he loves white people; he loves you Karuna and he loves your brother.'

The missionary paused and then he said very gently, 'Karuna, you were happy today because I am the same sort of colour as your brother. That's true, isn't it?'

'Yes,' said Karuna.

'Look at me carefully, Karuna. Look at my hair and look at my eyes. I am not really the same, am I?'

Karuna looked and felt as if all her happiness was being taken away again. Why did the missionary have to talk like this? She felt angry with him.

'Listen to me Karuna,' and the missionary's voice was very gentle. 'Do not pretend to yourself that your brother will grow up to be strong and healthy like other men. He is not strong and his eyes will never be strong. He cannot help it and neither can you. Your Mummy and Daddy cannot help it. All that you can do is to go on loving your brother and caring for him. I know that you do that already. But listen Karuna, I have told you that God loves white people as well as brown people. God also loves weak people as well as strong people. God loves your brother Karuna and he loves you. He loves your Mummy and your Daddy. He loves you just as much as he loves anybody else. That is why Jesus came and was born at Bethlehem, and he has sent me on this Christmas Day to tell you.'

Karuna looked at the earnest face of the missionary

for a long time. He was beginning to feel a bit uncomfortable, and then her whole face lit up with a smile.

Barnabas was so excited that he suddenly burst out with 'Jai Christu' ('Victory to Christ') and although they were taken by surprise the people replied, 'Jai Christu'.

Barnabas cried out again, and the people replied more vigorously.

A third time Barnabas shouted and this time all the people shouted at the tops of their voices, 'Victory, victory, victory to Jesus!'

When everything was quiet again the missionary asked Barnabas to pray. When he had finished they all joined in the Lord's Prayer. Last of all, with his arm around Karuna's shoulder, the missionary asked for God's blessing for all of them.

'A happy Christmas and God bless you,' he said as he went on his way.

'A happy Christmas,' they called and then some of the women began to talk all at once to Karuna's mother, and some of the men began to talk to Karuna's father, and the children crowded round Karuna and her brother, and Karuna felt as if the dark cloud had lifted and gone away. She was warm and happy inside —which is how Jesus wants us to be at Christmas-time.